A Collector's Guide to...

Military Rifle Disassembly and Reassembly

Step-by-step color breakdowns for all your favorite surplus and vintage rifles!

by Stuart C. Mowbray & Joe Puleo

Mowbray Publishing • 54 East School Street • Woonsocket, RI 02895 USA • www.manatarmsbooks.com

To order more copies of this book or to carry it in your store or gunshop, call 1-800-999-4697 or email: orders@manatarmsbooks.com. We carry a full line of fine gun collecting books; a free catalog is available upon request.

Stuart C. Mowbray and Joseph V. Puleo
    A Collector's Guide to Military Rifle Disassembly and Reassembly
54 East School St., Woonsocket, R.I. 02895: ANDREW MOWBRAY INC. — PUBLISHERS
    304 pp.

ISBN: 1-931464-32-4

To receive a free catalog of other fine gun and sword publications, call 1-800-999-4697.

Printed in China.   9 8 7 6 5 4 3 2 1

The Authors Would Like to Acknowledge Assistance from:
Scott Duff, John Wall, Steve Kehaya, Bruce N. Canfield, Mark Keefe, Barry DeLong, Dusan Farrington, Doss White, Evans Kavallines, Phil Schrier, Richard Johnson, Dennis Kroh, George Layman, Samco Global, Century International Arms, George A. Beaven, Frank van Binnendijk, Herbert G. Houze, Vince Rausch, Donald St.Germain, Charles Underwood, the members of Sayles Hill Rod and Gun Club, the late Donald B. Webster, Ernest Potter, Val Forgett, Paul Scarlata, Al Frasca, John McAulay, Scott Hartsell, and our friends on www.gunboards.com.

Important Notice: The descriptions, illustrations, comments and technical data presented in this book are based upon the unique experiences of the authors, including conditions and circumstances that are not all reported. These experiences, conditions and circumstances can not be duplicated exactly by the reader. Since each gun is unique and the experiences of the reader would almost certainly differ from that of the authors, the reader is warned against using the information in this book as practical directions or instructions. The authors and publisher accept no responsibility for any losses, damages, results, injuries or accidents. Never load or shoot a used or reassembled firearm without having it checked by a gunsmith. Also refer to the safety note on page 8.

YOUR RIFLE LOCATOR

The French M1866 Chassepot — 11

M1867/77 Austrian Werndl — 17

The Remington Rolling Block — 29

The Peabody Rifle — 35

British .577 Snider-Enfield — 41

The .45-70 Trapdoor Springfield — 57

Swiss Vetterli — 63

U.S. Model 1882 Chaffee-Reece — 69

The French Gras — 81

Russian Berdan Model 1870 — 85

Mauser Model 1871 and 1871/84 — 89

Portuguese M1886 Kropatschek — 95

Dutch Model 1871/88 Beaumont Vitali — 101

British .577-450 Martini-Henry — 107

German Gew. 1888 "Commission" Rifle — 115

(Continued on the following page.)

The Krag-Jorgensen 121

The Early Mannlichers, Models 1886–90 131

Mannlicher M95 Rifle and Carbine 137

Mannlicher M1895 Turnbolt 143

Italian Carcano 149

Model 1891 Mausers 155

Mauser Rifles and Carbines, M1892–96 159

1898 Mauser Rifles and 98k Carbines 165

The Mukden Type 13 Mauser 177

The Siamese M1903 (Type 45) Mauser 179

The U.S. Model 1903 Springfield 183

Portuguese M1904 Mauser-Vergueiro 189

Italian Vetterli Rifles and Carbines 195

French Lebel 201

French Berthier Model 1916 207

Enfield P14 and U.S. Model 1917 211

Enfield No. 1, Mark III 217

Enfield No. 4, Mark I* 227

Arisaka Type 44 Carbine 233

Arisaka Type 38 and Type 99 Rifles 235

Russian Mosin-Nagant Rifles & Carbines 241

Finnish Mosin-Nagant Rifles & Carbines 247

Swiss K31 Schmidt Rubin Carbine 253

Earlier Schmidt Rubin Longarms 259

Canadian Ross Rifles 261

M1 Garand 267

M1 Carbine 271

French MAS Model 1936 277

The SKS 281

Ljungman AG-42B - Egyptian Hakim 287

The Fabrique Nationale FN 49 291

The AK47 297

The Rashid 301

Austrian Mannlicher carbines in storage at Century International Arms, the world's largest importer of military rifles.

Introduction

In basic training, recruits are usually taught how to field strip their weapons. Sometimes this is done as a timed test, occasionally blindfolded. To civilians, this might seem like a strange waste of time, learning how to take a rifle apart to its basic components at rapid speed. "How often is this skill actually required in the field?", they might ask. The answer is "almost never." In combat, if a weapon jams or experiences mechanical failure, there usually isn't time to take it apart and locate the problem. During such pressure-filled moments, malfunctioning rifles are generally set aside and replaced by secondary weapons. When soldiers take their weapons to pieces, it is usually for routine cleaning and lubrication, which doesn't need to be done particularly fast (or blindfolded, for that matter).

But this doesn't mean that the rapid disassembly drill is meaningless. If you are going to depend upon a tool, then it is always a good idea to have an intimate understanding of its construction and operation. Intimacy breeds respect. Intimacy creates a bond of trust. And with mechanical tasks like disassembly, intimacy is achieved through repetition — which is best measured by speed of operation. If you can disassemble a rifle very quickly, this means that you have done it a lot. The speed is proof of repetition and confirms the required level of intimacy.

Just like soldiers, collectors of military weapons can gain knowledge of their rifles by taking them apart and then reassembling them. And it isn't just for cleaning and lubrication. Nothing can teach you more about a rifle's construction than taking it to pieces.

It is surprising how few collectors today understand the basic operation of the rifles they collect. They know how the guns work, of course, but if challenged to explain what the parts of the bolt do, or what the inside of a tubular magazine looks like, many of them would be totally lost. This is where

A U.S. Marine blackens the front sight of his M1 Garand.

the intimacy developed through disassembly can open up whole new horizons of knowledge for collectors. What are a rifle's strong points? Its weaknesses? Is it a simple design or an overly complex one? Was it made with care? Was it repaired or altered while in service? Often, these are questions that can only be answered through disassembly.

But many of the rifles in our collections are in pristine condition. Sometimes, they are so mint that we would hesitate to loosen a single screw. That's where this book comes in! We have done the dirty work for you. Step-by-step, we take you through the whole process — and not with smeary pictures or confusing diagrams, but with huge, clear photos that show everything, printed on the highest quality paper available. In fact, it is our hope that this book will show the true beauty of historical military rifles. Some folks think that military rifles, especially surplus rifles, are ugly. It is our aim to show you not only how Italian Vetterlis are taken apart (for instance), but also just how well they are made and how visually appealing they can be, both assembled and in component parts. To reenforce this concept that rifles are attractive, we will begin each section with a dramatic "beauty shot" portrait of the weapon to be disassembled, taken in a professional photo studio.

German infantry at work cleaning their rifles. Note the smocks.

A soldier's handkerchief depicting the German Gew. 88 "Commission" Rifle. Be aware that reproductions of these exist, most of which have the logo and address of a German military museum printed in the upper left hand corner. The photos of this example have had the red "pumped up" so that it will look as it did when new. The actual handkerchief has faded to an orange color from light damage.

were never intended to be taken apart, and if that is the case, then we considered it beyond the scope of this book.

How were the rifles chosen? Basically, we have tried to include as many as we could. Other disassembly guides that we have owned over the years have had only a token representation of military rifles (most of which were sporterized), and seemed to be more concerned with hunting guns than the ones we cared about. They also usually concentrated on common weapons that we already knew inside and out, while totally ignoring the rare rifle systems that were more likely to puzzle us. That isn't the case here! We have tried to make the book that we always wanted to own ourselves...one that shows the guns that military rifle collectors like you and I really want to see. So while there may be a place for deer rifles, you aren't going to find any in these pages.

One other thing that you will notice about this book, unlike some others, is that the disassembly only goes so far. That's because taking some stuff off just seems silly. Do you really need to see us unscrew two slotted screws to remove a rear sight that no one would ever need to take off anyway? We don't think so, and we hope you agree. So, if during the disassembly of these guns we reached a point where we didn't think it was worth going further... we stopped. And if we thought that further disassembly was going to damage the gun, then we also stopped. This was a judgement call, so bear with us when you want to see the action removed from the buttstock of an Enfield and we quit after breaking two screwdrivers trying to get it off. Some things

An Italian sergeant instructs fascist recruits on how to present arms.

Disclaimer and Important Notes About Safety:

This book should not in any way be considered a replacement for a competent gunsmith. Do not load or shoot any firearm before having it inspected by a trained professional gunsmith. Do not handle any firearm unless you are trained to do so. Never break any laws. Each disassembly or reassembly is a unique event and each rifle is different. Many rifles have alterations, damage, wear or unexpected features that will make them respond differently than the examples shown here. Because the reader could never duplicate exactly all of the conditions experienced by the authors, the reader is warned against using the contents of this book as instructions. Note also that all rifles have springs and other mechanical parts, some quite sharp, that can cause injury to even the most careful mechanic. This book's only purpose is to depict a series of the authors' experiences for the historical education and entertainment of the reader. The authors and publisher make no recommendation about whether a reader should disassemble his or her own rifle and will take no responsibility for any unfortunate events that may take place to either people or property should the activities depicted in this book be attempted by the reader. While reasonable efforts have been made to make this book accurate, it is almost certain that some mistakes have been included. Also, some steps of disassembly or reassembly may have been left out, either unintentionally or because they were thought overly obvious. In any disassembly, the first step should always be to make sure that the weapon is pointed in a safe direction, is unloaded and that the barrel, magazine and receiver are clear. The last step in any reassembly should be to have the firearm inspected by a trained gunsmith before it is loaded with ammunition or given to someone who might load it with ammunition. The authors and publisher disclaim responsibility for any accidents. **FIREARMS SAFETY IS THE SOLE RESPONSIBILITY OF THE PERSON HANDLING THE FIREARM. ALWAYS TREAT ALL FIREARMS AS IF THEY WERE LOADED.**

If you don't see one of your favorite military models it means one of two things: either it was more or less identical to another rifle already in this book (for instance, just how many Mauser 98 clones do we really need to show?); or we simply could not find an example to include. Our collections are pretty large, but they aren't complete. And while lots of our fellow collectors are eager to have their favorite rifle appear in a fancy book like this, very few of them are willing to have the gun taken to pieces for that purpose. To those who have, we say "thank you."

Back in the 1890s, it was popular for mothers to give their soldier sons handkerchiefs that were printed with all the things that a new recruit was expected to learn. These factory-made gifts included all the standard commands, bugle calls, symbols of rank, flag signals and other information that was considered essential to a new soldier's survival. But what was the largest, most prominent feature of these handkerchiefs? The rifle disassembly drawings. Like those moms of 120 years

WWI French reservists with their Model 1886 Lebel rifles.

A Belgian lancer with his M1889 Mauser carbine. Those Belgians sure know their hats!

ago, we have the same kind of hopes that this book will equip you with the information you need to understand the rifles you collect better and to avoid some of the common misconceptions that we all get fooled by once in a while.

For us, it has been a real pleasure to get to take so many fine rifles to pieces in a relatively short amount of time. This was truly educational and gave an almost unique opportunity for comparison, one rifle to another. During this process, we came to understand a few things. First of all, it became clear that major industrial nations did not arm their troops with inferior or cheap weapons. The rifles issued by these countries were of consistently good quality, with cost being of secondary importance compared to performance and durability. Even the military rifles of Italy, which have been disparaged in some collecting circles, are very well made — their insides showing careful workmanship. And nations with no arms-making facilities of their own could still manage to purchase remarkably high quality arms, often on a limited budget — the Chilean M1895 Mausers being an excellent example.

In fact, the basic materials and strength of most rifle designs are quite remarkable...especially when compared to just about any consumer product that you can imagine. It was totally common for military rifles to be rebuilt three or more times without significant loss of battle worthiness. That's multiple generations of service! How long do you think your computer or fax machine of today will last?

Irish irregulars (I.R.A. or Loyalist) armed with SMLE rifles. c.1920s.

News photo of female Communist Chinese soldiers on the run with their SKS carbines and fixed bayonets.

The designers put *a lot* of thought into these guns. When you think about it, the lives of their families could literally depend upon the quality of their engineering...and it shows. For instance, on many of the more carefully designed rifles, it is impossible to confuse parts during reassembly. The wrong screw will not fit in the wrong hole and parts cannot be put together backwards. That's why we illustrate reassembly highlights rather than showing every step of reassembly. Often, it is almost impossible to do it wrong.

Another thing we observed was that as military rifles evolved they featured fewer parts — but each of those parts tended to be of more complicated manufacture. As a result, disassembly of modern rifles is far simpler than disassembly of earlier designs. Perhaps not coincidentally, it is quite clear that arms makers were not designing rifles that soldiers were intended to field strip by themselves until the end of the 19th century, at the earliest. Many parts even required special armorer's tools particularly intended to prevent soldiers from disassembling their rifles beyond a certain point.

Interestingly, as a general rule, we noticed that the more literate the country, the more complicated the gun — but this did not necessarily convert into more battle-worthy weapons. The Mosin-Nagant, for instance, is a very simple weapon, but an excellent combat rifle. The strength of this design is attested to by the fact that Finland (a nation that prides itself upon its marksmanship) was still making target rifles from Czarist actions as late as the 1970s.

After all this, which rifle did we come away admiring the most? We can already hear the protests from Mauser fans, but for us it was not the winner. Without question, our "top gun" was the K31 Schmidt-Rubin. The fact that this is arguably the most accurate rifle ever issued to regular line infantry comes as no surprise to us after working on this project. What a gem of a rifle! It is smooth to operate, beautifully made and has a rapid, straight-pull action. And unlike almost all other bolt rifles, it can easily be operated left-handed. Speaking of which, it's time for us to grab our K31s and head out to the shooting range. Happy collecting! ❏

About the Authors...

Stuart C. Mowbray is editor of *Gun Collector* magazine, the National Rifle Association's official journal for arms collectors. He is also author of *331+ Essential Tips & Tricks: A How-To Guide for the Gun Collector*. Joe Puleo is contributing technical editor for the same publication.

If you like this book, then you will almost certainly want to subscribe to *Gun Collector*, a full color magazine that is not available as part of your NRA membership and requires a separate subscription. Contact 1-800-999-4697, orders@manatarmsbooks.com or www.manatarmsbooks.com for more information.

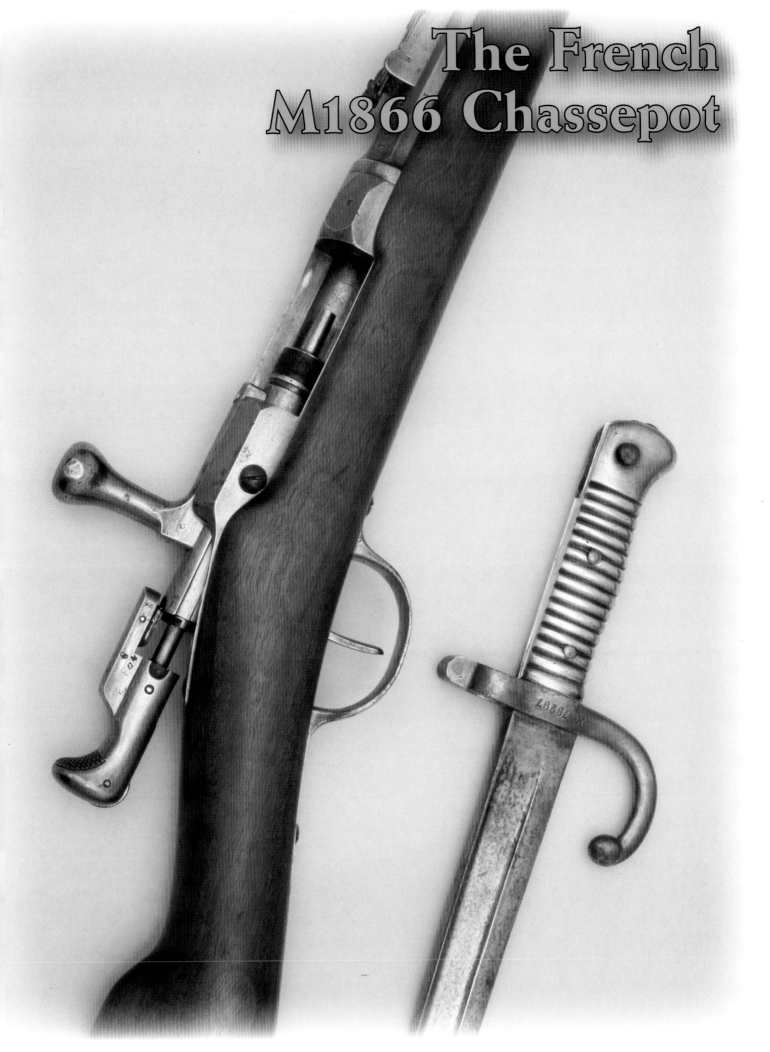

STEP 1

This early rifle does not have a clear way to determine whether it is loaded before cocking it, which is a safety concern requiring extra careful handling. To open the action and check that no ammunition is present, the rifle is cocked with the thumb while the muzzle is pointed in a safe direction. Fingers are kept clear of the triggerguard.

STEP 2

The bolt handle is rotated to its 12 o'clock position and the bolt is carefully drawn back. The breech and barrel are carefully checked for ammunition or other obstructions.

STEP 3

The bolt-retaining screw is loosened all of the way (i.e., to its last thread, freeing the bolt) or removed entirely.

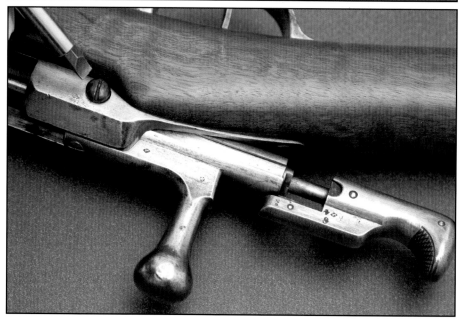

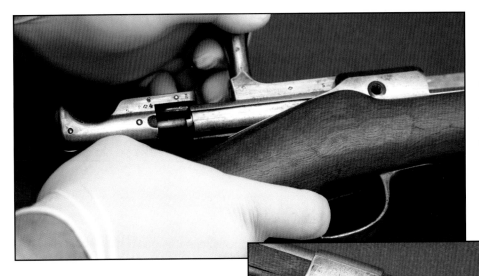

STEP 4

With the trigger depressed, the bolt is grasped by its handle and drawn to the rear until it is fully clear of the rifle.

STEP 5

The ramrod is removed from its channel.

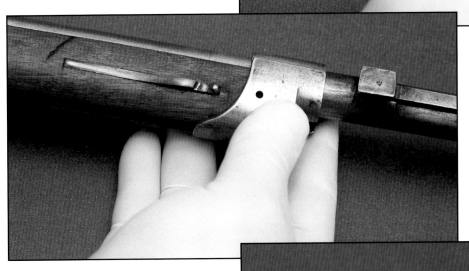

STEP 6

The two barrel bands are removed, front then rear. There is a trick to removing the front one. See step 7 below.

STEP 7

The front barrel band must be rotated around the bayonet lugs and sight before it will slide off of the muzzle. Patience is required, but it does work.

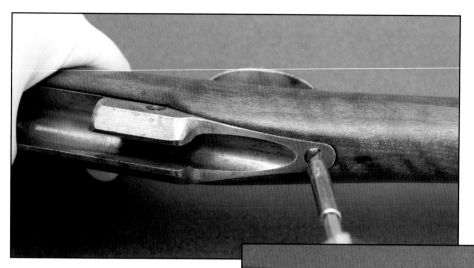

STEP 8

The tang screw is removed.

STEP 9

The barreled action can now be removed from the stock.

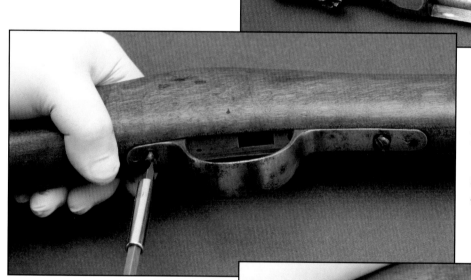

STEP 10

The triggerguard is removed after unscrewing two wood screws.

STEP 11

Two screws retain the rear sling swivel, and can be removed if desired.

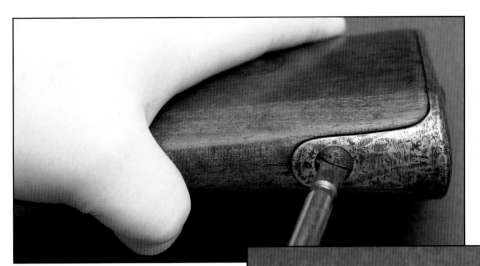

STEP 12

Two more screws must be dealt with in order to remove the buttplate.

STEP 13

The trigger spring (a long strip of steel at the bottom of the action) is secured with a square-headed screw. This, in turn, is held in place by a smaller round-headed set-screw, which must be removed before the square-headed screw will rotate.

STEP 14

The trigger can be dislodged from the trigger spring by drifting out the pin that holds them together. However, there are few reasons why this would ever need to be done.

Model 1866 Bolt

Disassembly:

The tension on the mainspring is released by turning the cocking piece 90 degrees to the left or right of the bolt. The gasket retaining screw is now removed.

The gasket assembly is slid off of the firing needle.

The nut at the middle of the bolt is unscrewed using a wrench. (We used a 5/16 inch ignition wrench with the sides ground to a slightly thinner profile.)

With the nut thus unscrewed to show all of its threads, but still in place, the front half of the bolt slides off.

This view is a close-up of the nut showing its threads as described in the step above.

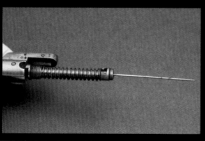

Now that the front half of the bolt has been removed, the mechanical design of the needle-fire system can be appreciated. Neat, huh?

Next, the needle is removed by sliding off the keeper at its base.

Once removed, the two pieces come loose and can be separated.

The spring can now be taken off.

Then the nut can follow.

The bolt is now disassembled to its basic component parts. The back part of the bolt can be further disassembled by drifting out pins, but this is not recommended.

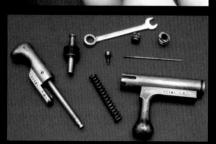

Reassembly Note:

In order to replace the bolt in the rifle (once it has been reassembled) it must be returned to its full cock position.

STEP 1

First, it is ensured that the rifle is not loaded. Note that this is a Model 1867/77 Jaeger Rifle, First Type. However, differences between the various Werndls are slight and are mostly relegated to rechambering and sight replacements. The one major exception is the Model 1873, which has its hammer inside the lockplate.

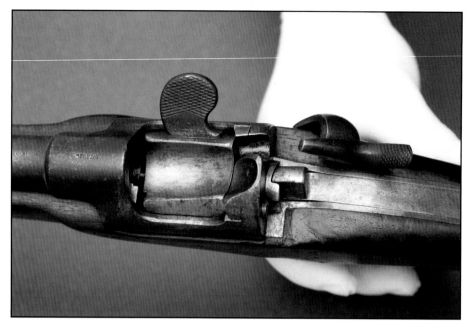

STEP 2

The cleaning rod is unscrewed and removed.

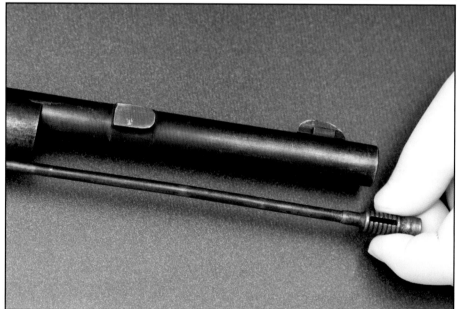

STEP 3

The nose cap on the Werndl actually acts as a barrel band. It is removed by taking out the screw shown and sliding the cap forward and off, dodging the sight and bayonet lug on the way.

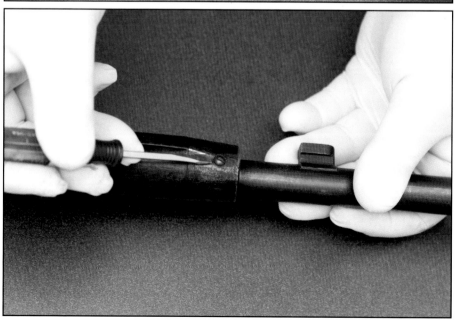

STEP 4

If, in the previous step, the nose cap is tight, it can be tapped off using a small block of wood and a plastic-headed hammer.

STEP 5

The forward barrel band is loosened and the band slid forward and removed. The rear barrel band (not shown) requires that its screw be removed entirely before it can be sprung open, slid forward and off.

STEP 6

The hammer is brought to full cock as shown. This is necessary in order to clear the breechblock.

STEP 7

The screw forward of the hammer is removed.

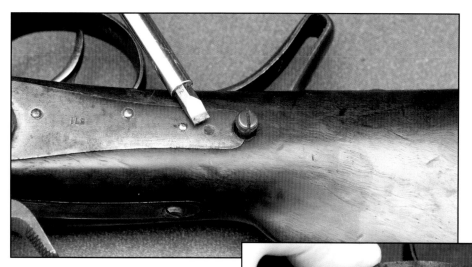

STEP 8

The wood screw at the rear of the lock is removed.

STEP 9

The lock is gently lifted out of its mortise. If tight, the hammer is gently tapped with a plastic hammer, taking care not to chip the wood around the lockplate.

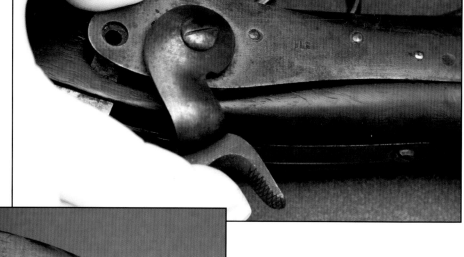

STEP 10

The screws at the front of the triggerguard (shown left) and at the rear of the tang (shown right) are removed.

STEP 11

The breechblock spring is lifted off, exposing the body of the tang. This is an interesting feature and unlike most other rifles.

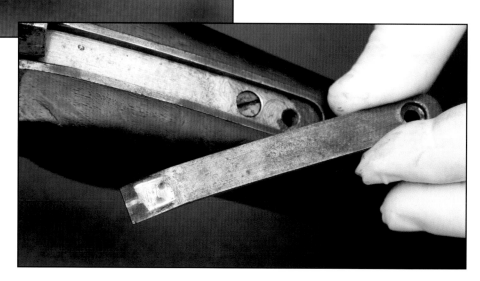

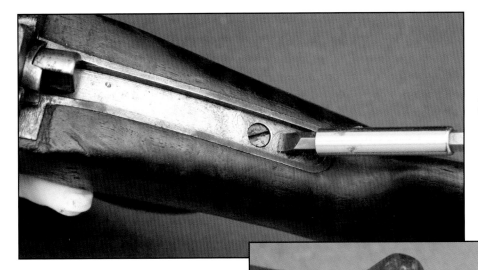

STEP 12
The tang screw is removed.

STEP 13
The wood screw at the rear of the triggerguard is taken out.

STEP 14
The triggerguard is now pulled down and off the rifle. Note the hook at the front of the triggerguard bow, which must be cleared in this process.

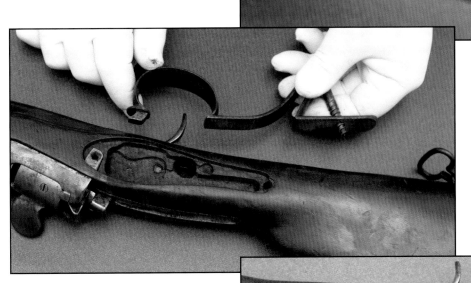

STEP 15
The breech and barrel are lifted out of the stock. If tight, gentle tapping at the breech end may be required.

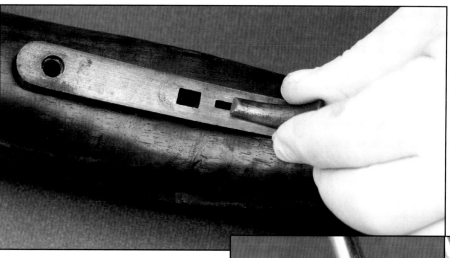

STEP 16

The trigger plate is lifted out. In this case, it was tight and the trigger itself needed to be tapped backwards with a plastic-headed hammer. Overall, this rifle was very tight and required a lot of gentle "encouragement."

STEP 17

The sling swivel and buttplate are removed using the obvious screws. Note that the tang of the buttplate has a unit marking, in this case indicating issue to the 26th Regiment of Infantry, Ersatz Battalion, Second Company. It was weapon Number 77.

STEP 18

The trigger is removed by taking out the screw shown.

STEP 19

This is what the trigger and trigger plate look like when disassembled. Construction is simple compared to many other rifles in this book, but it is very well made.

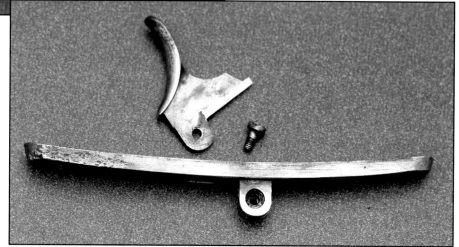

STEP 20

The lock is brought to full cock — the position shown here.

STEP 21

A mainspring vise is employed as shown to squeeze the main spring and hold it compressed.

STEP 22

The two screws at the front of the bridle are removed. This photo shows one out and another left to be dealt with.

STEP 23

The mainspring is removed by gently wiggling the vise and trying to pull it away from the lockplate. There is a pin in the spring that sticks into a hole in the lockplate and this can require some patience. In this case, it was quite difficult — refer to the next two steps for details.

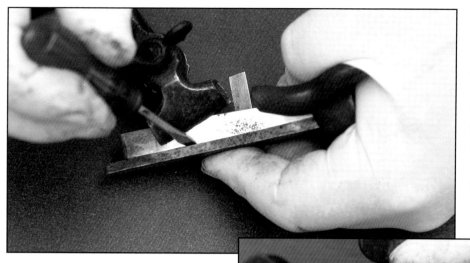

STEP 24

With the spring compressed, a small screwdriver is inserted as an attempt to wedge the spring away from the lockplate. This usually works, but in this case was unsuccessful.

STEP 25

As a next resort, the spring's pin (projecting through the lockplate) was drifted out. This was effective in removing the spring. Note that it is a domed pin and requires a punch made for this purpose.

STEP 26

Now that the pin is out, the mainspring is lifted up and the claws at its front unhooked from the stirrup.

STEP 27

The sear screw is now removed. This allows the bridle and sear to come free.

STEP 28

The hammer screw is taken out. When this is done, on the other side of the lock, the tumbler and the stirrup fall out.

STEP 29

This is what the disassembled lock looks like. Now we move on to the action.

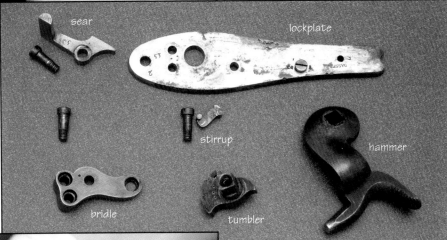

sear

lockplate

stirrup

hammer

bridle

tumbler

STEP 30

The screw shown here is taken out.

STEP 31

The plate at the rear of the breech is removed by pushing it straight up. This part is almost always very tight. It can require a good deal of judicious persuasion. It would be easy to damage the rifle trying to force it out.

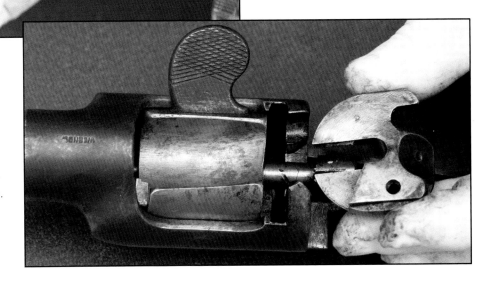

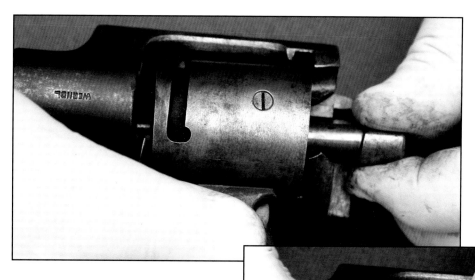

STEP 32

The breechblock (the big cylindrical part) is twisted as shown and lifted out of the breech.

STEP 33

The extractor can now be removed. The photo shows it taken out...it came from the left portion of the breech.

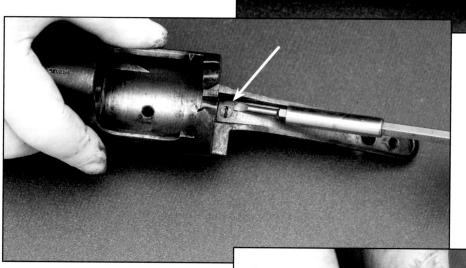

STEP 34

The small screw (see arrow) that retains the lower bearing for the breechblock is taken out.

STEP 35

The bearing is removed. This came from the slot indicated in the photo by an arrow. It was tapped towards the barrel with a wooden dowel to loosen it. (It can't come up straight...it has to go forward.)

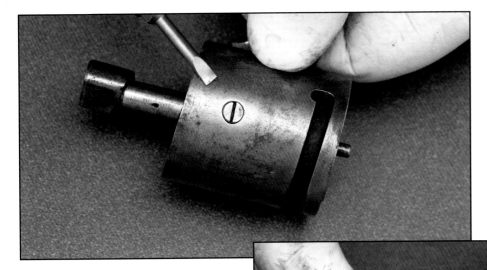

STEP 36

The firing pin retaining screw is removed.

STEP 37

The firing pin and its spring can now be pulled out as shown on the left side of the photo.

REASSEMBLING THE LOCK

STEP 38

The stirrup (which may or may not have fallen off the tumbler) can be replaced as shown.

STEP 39

The tumbler, bridle and sear are replaced on the lock plate. Their screws are then put in place and tightened as shown in this photo.

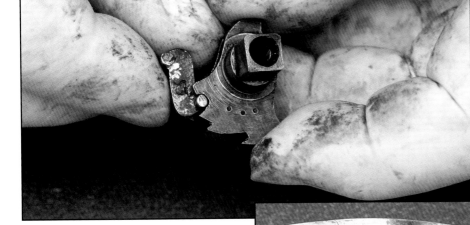

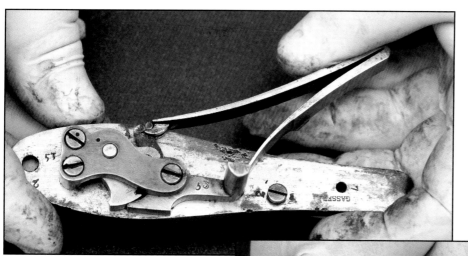

STEP 40

The claws at the tip of the mainspring are hooked onto the stirrup as shown.

STEP 41

The bent portion of the mainspring can now be pushed down and back until its pin lines up with the hole in the lockplate, and then tapped fully into place using a plastic-headed hammer. In this case, it required a number of tries and a good deal of hand strength.

STEP 42

This is what the mainspring looks like when fully replaced.

STEP 43

The hammer screw can now be replaced and tightened with the hammer in the position shown. Further reassembly of the rifle is a relatively simple reversal of the disassembly steps.

The Remington Rolling Block

STEP 1

It is confirmed that the rifle is unloaded and that the barrel is empty. This particular rolling block rifle is a New York State model, which means that it has an oversized hammer and a safety mechanism allowing the rifle to be loaded at half cock, which is not found on most other rifles.

STEP 2

Most Rolling Block cleaning rods are threaded to screw into a small block on the front of the action. If the rod cannot be readily withdrawn, it must be turned as if unscrewing it.

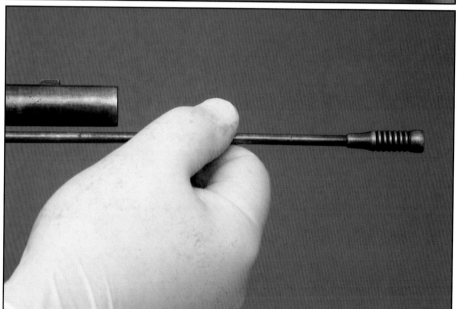

STEP 3

The barrel band retaining springs are depressed and the three barrel bands are slid off the rifle, starting with the one closest to the muzzle. Care is taken not to damage any wood.

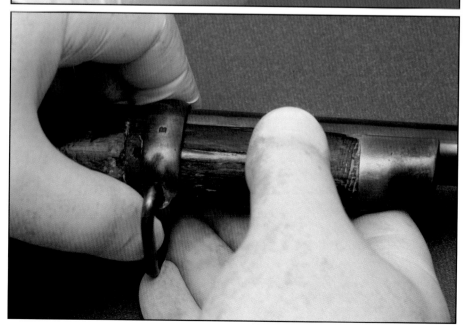

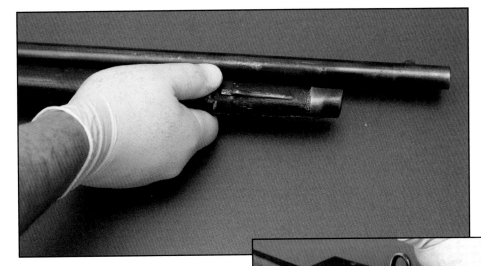

STEP 4

From the muzzle end, the stock and barrel are gently separated from each other and the forend pulled forward. There is a small tab of wood that fits into the front of the action so it must be pulled forward slightly in order to be removed.

STEP 5

The tang screw is carefully removed.

STEP 6

The buttstock slides off of the metal frame. Sometimes, a few light taps on the triggerguard with a plastic hammer (while holding the stock so it doesn't move) are necessary to loosen this piece.

STEP 7

The two lower screws on the frame are removed. These screws are often very tight. The condition of these screws is an important factor in valuing Rolling Blocks, so great care is taken not to damage the screw slots.

Technical Note:
While we prefer to take the triggerguard off before the block and hammer. the factory-recommended method was to take the triggerguard off last. Some people find the "factory" order easier during disassembly.

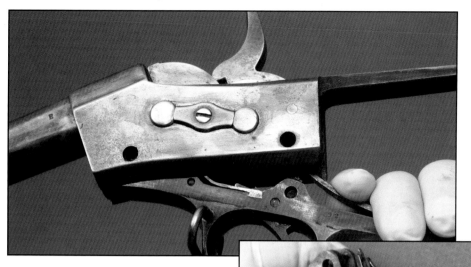

STEP 8

The trigger assembly can now be removed. Further disassembly requires drifting out the two pins that hold the parts in place. Since it is quite easy to clean these parts in place, disassembly isn't usually necessary.

STEP 9

The trigger assembly. This is the version used on the U.S. M1871 and the New York contract rifles. Another type also exists and is more common. See the note at the end of this section.

STEP 10

The screw and keeper on the left side of the frame are now removed.

STEP 11

The heavy pin that holds the breech block can now be withdrawn. This usually comes out easily.

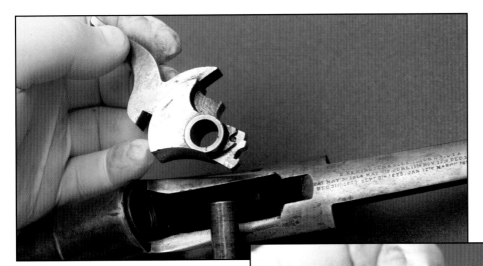

STEP 12

The pin that holds the hammer is also removed now.

STEP 13

The extractor, mounted on the left side of the breech block, comes off readily.

Rolling Blocks with Differences

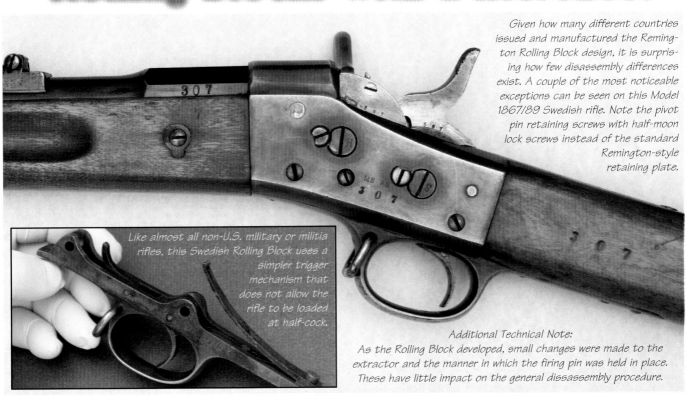

Given how many different countries issued and manufactured the Remington Rolling Block design, it is surprising how few disassembly differences exist. A couple of the most noticeable exceptions can be seen on this Model 1867/89 Swedish rifle. Note the pivot pin retaining screws with half-moon lock screws instead of the standard Remington-style retaining plate.

Like almost all non-U.S. military or militia rifles, this Swedish Rolling Block uses a simpler trigger mechanism that does not allow the rifle to be loaded at half-cock.

Additional Technical Note:
As the Rolling Block developed, small changes were made to the extractor and the manner in which the firing pin was held in place. These have little impact on the general disassembly procedure.

Selected Reassembly Notes

STEP 14

Reassembly of the Rolling Block is simply a reversal of the disassembly steps. When replacing the trigger assembly, it seems easiest to align the rear hole first.

STEP 15

The rear screw is inserted and tightened a few threads. The front of the trigger assembly can now be pushed up into place, compressing the mainspring slightly.

STEP 16

The front screw is inserted. If the holes are aligned properly, both screws should go in with hand pressure.

STEP 17

Each screw was started a few threads and then both tightened gently, being careful not to damage the heads.

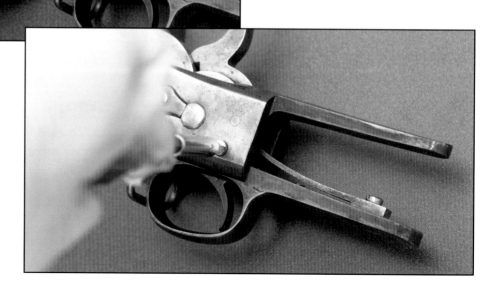

The Peabody Rifle

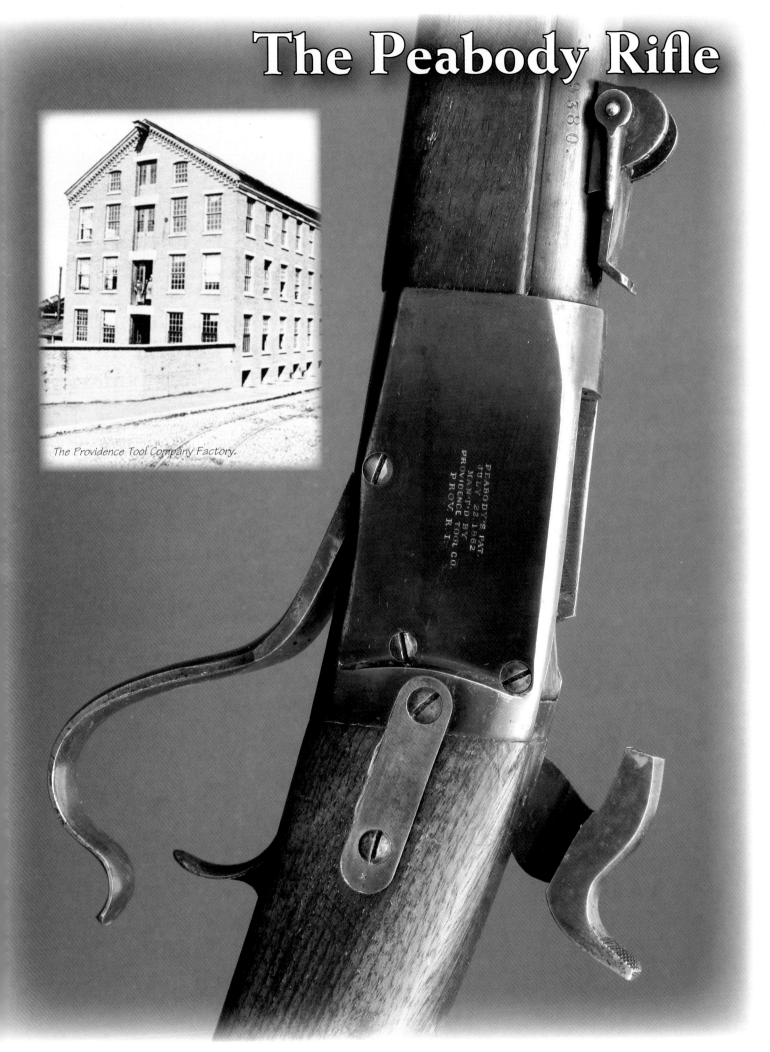

The Providence Tool Company Factory.

PEABODY'S PAT.
JULY 22 1862
MAN'F'D BY
PROVIDENCE TOOL CO.
PROV. R.I.

STEP 1

First, it is confirmed that the rifle is not loaded.

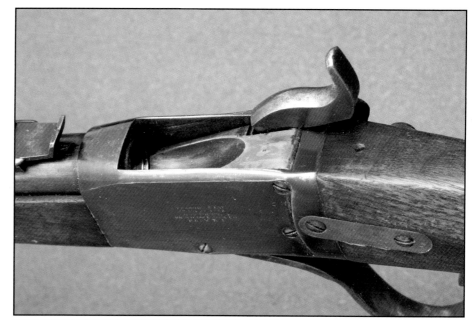

STEP 2

The cleaning rod is removed.

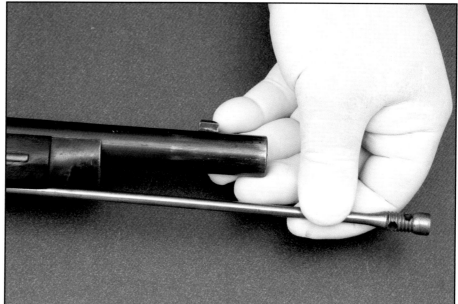

STEP 3

The front barrel band is removed by depressing its retaining spring and sliding it forward.

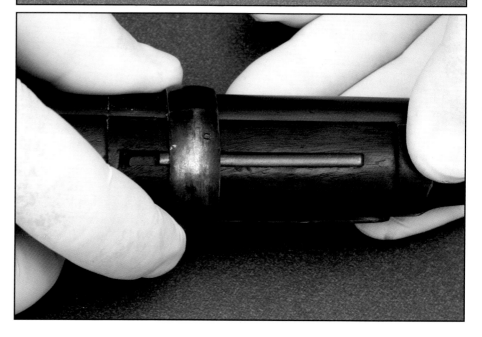

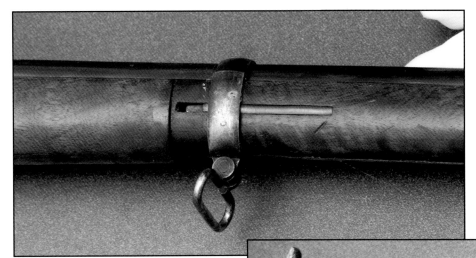

STEP 4

The rear barrel band is removed in the same manner as the front band.

STEP 5

The small screw ahead of the lever is removed (see arrow) allowing the forend to be pulled down and forward gently, taking care not to damage the two tabs of wood that project into the action.

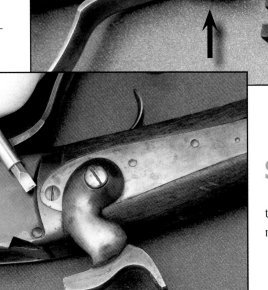

STEP 6

The hammer is cocked and the lock-retaining screw (which is now revealed) is taken out.

STEP 7

The screw at the rear of the lock, which enters from the left side, is removed. The plate connecting the stock to the action (see arrow) is not removed. It is a dummy used to take the place of the sling ring that is mounted on the carbine version of this arm.

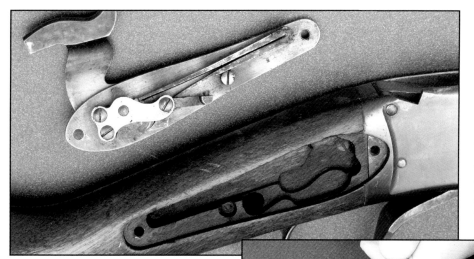

STEP 8

The lock is now gently lifted out of its inlet. The dissassembly steps for this lock are virtually identical to those used on the Werndl rifle described elsewhere in this book. For this reason, the lock will not be disassembled here.

STEP 9

The loading lever and the flat part in front of it are held in place with a screw, which is now removed.

STEP 10

The photograph at the left shows the lever and the plate that holds the extractor removed from the action.

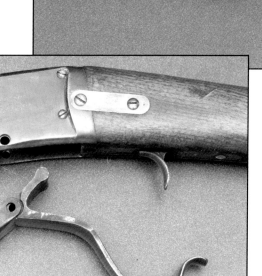

STEP 11

The screw that retains the breech block is removed. The block is under spring tension so it will pop up and out of the action when the screw is withdrawn.

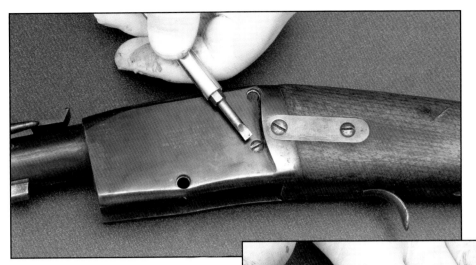

STEP 12

The last screw removed from the action holds a metal sleeve/roller in place inside the action.

STEP 13

The screw and sleeve/roller removed.

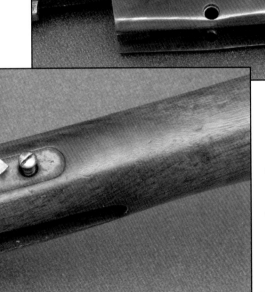

STEP 14

The screws retaining the trigger plate with its attached trigger are now taken out.

STEP 15

The trigger plate and trigger are lifted out of their inlet.

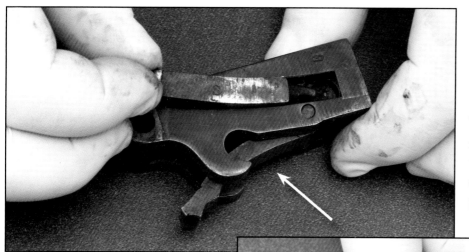

STEP 16

The firing pin can be lifted out of the breechblock. We chose not to further disassemble the breechblock as the lever (see arrow) is under considerable spring tension and we had reservations about being able to return it to its proper place.

REASSEMBLY NOTES
STEP 17

Reassembly is mostly a reversal of disassembly steps. The tricky part is shown here.

The screw holding the sleeve/roller is returned to the action.

STEP 18

The breechblock is inserted into the top of the action and pressed down with a thumb while its retaining screw is returned to its hole. This is under considerable tension and requires a good deal of hand strength to accomplish. At this point, the trigger plate and trigger is reattached.

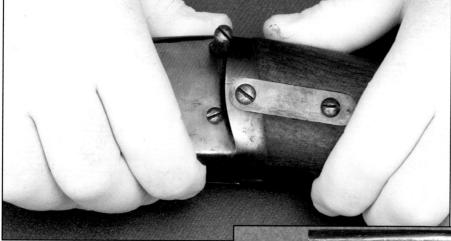

STEP 19

With the breechblock pushed into its open position (top photograph), the lever and plate holding the extractor are wiggled into place and their retaining screw returned to the action (bottom photograph).

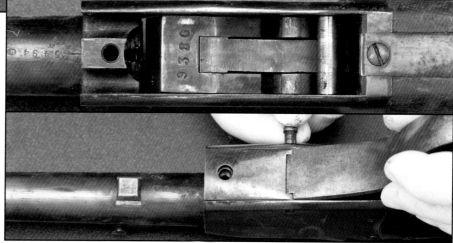

British .577
Snider-Enfield

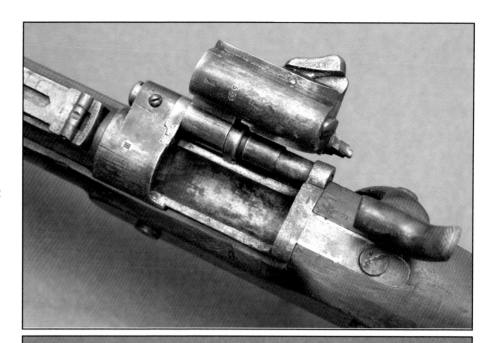

STEP 1

With the muzzle pointed in a safe direction, it is confirmed that the rifle is not loaded.

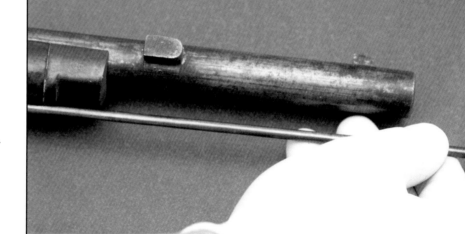

STEP 2

The cleaning rod is removed.

STEP 3

(left) The captured screw that tightens the front barrel band is loosened.

(right) The screw that tightens the rear barrel band is also loosened. These barrel band screws are not actually removed.

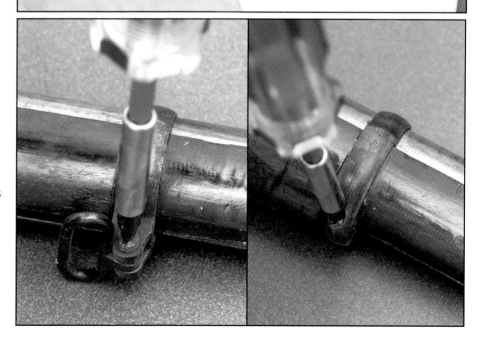

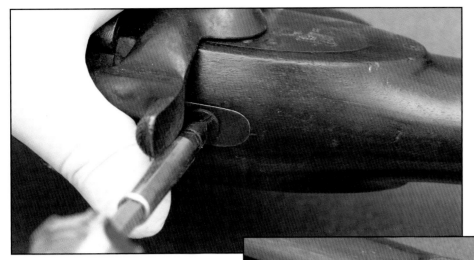

STEP 4

The barrel tang screw is removed. It should be noted that all of the screws in the Snider have narrower slots than those in most 20th-century military rifles and thus require thin-bladed screwdrivers.

STEP 5

The hammer is now cocked to bring it away from the breech.

The barrel and breech block assembly is then lifted from the stock.

STEP 6

The small screw/pin that retains the breech block hinge pin is removed.

STEP 7

The hinge pin is now withdrawn. It was quite tight on this example, so it was necessary to pry it forward slightly in order to loosen it.

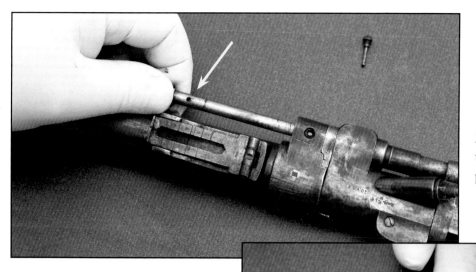

STEP 8

The hinge pin is withdrawn. Note the tiny hole (see arrow) in the hinge pin where the retaining pin passed through.

STEP 9

The extractor spring and its two cover pieces are now removed, being careful to hold them tightly as they are under spring tension.

STEP 10

The thumb-operated release catch is now pressed in.

STEP 11

The breech block is now lifted out of the breech.

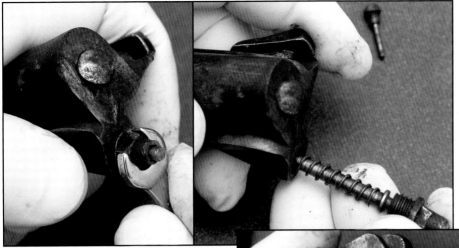

STEP 12

(left) A small wrench is used to loosen and remove the firing pin retaining nut.

(right) With the nut unscrewed, the firing pin and its spring are taken out of the breech block.

STEP 13

(left) The screw/pin that retains the thumb-operated catch for the breech block is loosened and removed.

(right) With its pin removed, the thumb piece can be slid out.

STEP 14

The catch and its spring are now released and can be slipped out of the rear of the breech block.

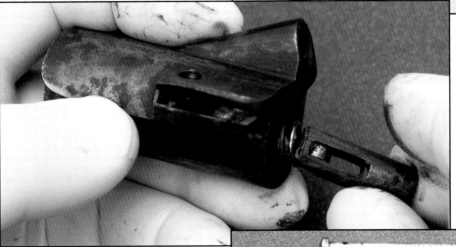

STEP 15

The Snider breech block disassembled.

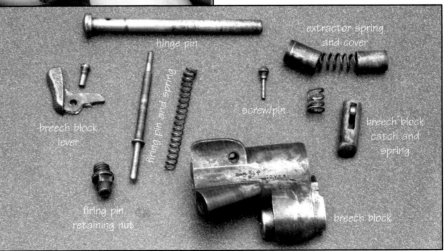

hinge pin

extractor spring and cover

breech block lever

firing pin and spring

screw/pin

breech block catch and spring

firing pin retaining nut

breech block

STEP 16

The two lock screws are now loosened two or three turns.

STEP 17

The lock is usually inlet very precisely and tight in the stock. In order to dislodge it without damaging the stock, the loosened screws are gently tapped with a plastic hammer.

STEP 18

Once loosened, the lock is gently lifted from its inlet.

STEP 19

The wood screws that retain the triggerguard are now removed.

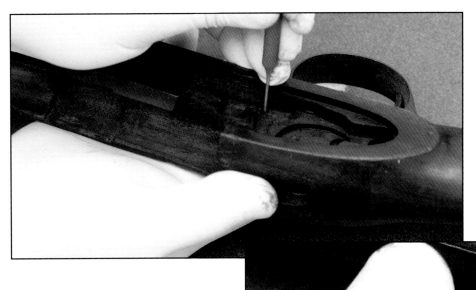

STEP 20

The front of the triggerguard is retained with a pin that passes through the stock. It should be removed only if absolutely necessary as it is easy to chip or otherwise damage the stock.

STEP 21

The rear sling swivel, the base of which consists of a large wood screw, is now removed. The triggerguard can then be taken off.

STEP 22

The buttplate can be removed by taking out its two retaining screws.

STEP 23

In order to disassemble the lock, the hammer is first brought to full cock.

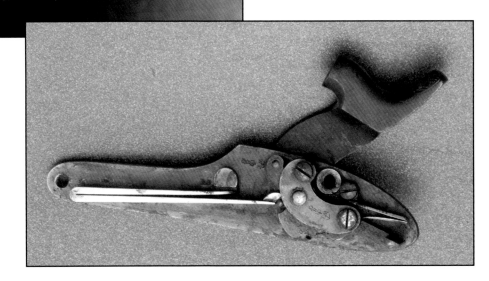

STEP 24

The mainspring is secured with an appropriate hand vice. It is tightened until pressure is relieved, but not so much as to crush it or risk breakage.

STEP 25

Once the spring is compressed, the sear is pushed up (see right thumb in photo) and the hammer is lowered all the way to its uncocked position.

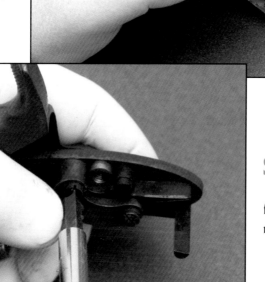

STEP 26

The bridle screw (see picture for location) is loosened and removed.

STEP 27

The sear screw is loosened two or three turns, but not removed.

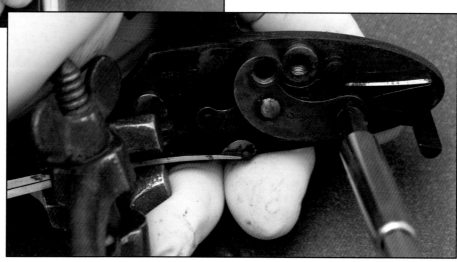

STEP 28

The sear spring screw (see photo) is loosened two turns, but not removed.

STEP 29

The sear spring is now pulled away from the lockplate by delicately using the end of a screwdriver to pry at the end of the spring (where it bends). The tab connecting the spring to the lockplate pops out, allowing the spring to move freely.

STEP 30

Now that the sear spring is loose, the sear spring screw is removed and both pieces taken off.

STEP 31

The sear screw may now be taken out by hand.

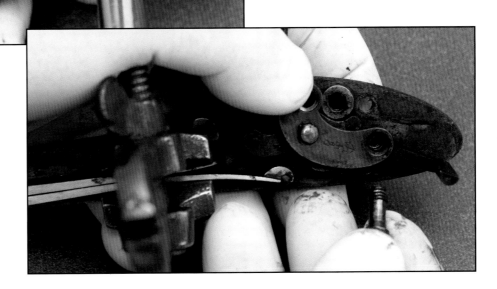

STEP 32

The sear is removed.

STEP 33

The bridle is lifted off.

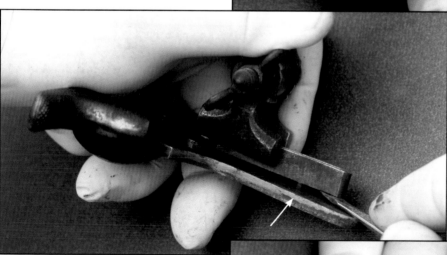

STEP 34

The back of the mainspring is now pulled up and away from the lockplate. It may be necessary to gently pry its pin (see arrow) out of its corresponding hole in the lockplate.

STEP 35

The mainspring can now be removed by lifting the claw at its end off of the stirrup.

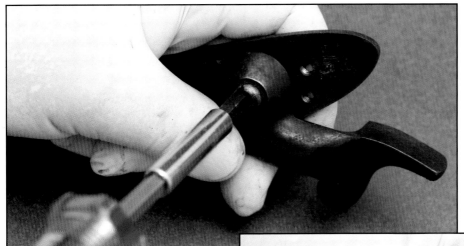

STEP 36

The hammer-retaining screw is taken out.

STEP 37

The hammer is removed. Sometimes this requires the use of a punch. If this is done, it is critical that the punch be smaller than the hole so that it does not touch the threads.

STEP 38

The tumbler (with its attached stirrup) is lifted off.

STEP 39

The lock disassembled.

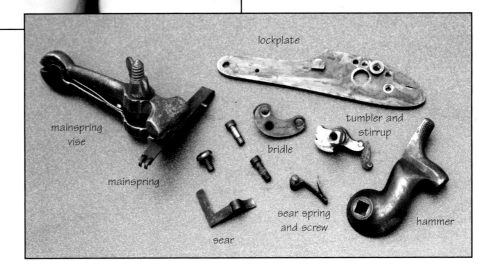

lockplate

mainspring vise

tumbler and stirrup

bridle

mainspring

sear spring and screw

hammer

sear

LOCK REASSEMBLY

STEP 40

The tumbler and stirrup are replaced in the lockplate.

STEP 41

The bridle is placed over the tumbler as shown.

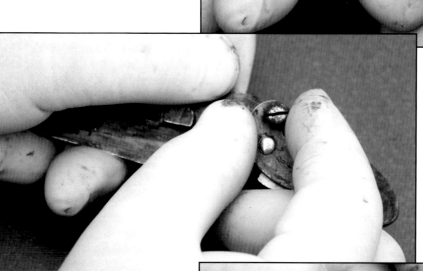

STEP 42

The bridle screw is inserted two or three turns as shown — but not tightened.

STEP 43

The sear is lined up with the hole in the bridle and the hole in the lockplate.

STEP 44

The sear screw is inserted, screwed in two or three turns, but not tightened.

STEP 45

The hole at the back of the sear spring is lined up and very loosely attached using the sear spring screw as shown. This screw is not tightened yet.

STEP 46

The sear spring screw is now tightened just enough to bring the tab at the back of the spring up against the lockplate. The position shown in the photo is correct.

STEP 47

The end of the spring where it bends is now pushed down until the tab at its rear catches in its recess in the lockplate. Usually, this makes a snapping noise. The bridle screw, sear spring screw and sear screw are now tightened.

STEP 48

The hammer is pushed onto the square projection coming through the lockplate. This may require mild force.

STEP 49

The sear is pushed up (see bottom right corner of the photo) and the hammer then pushed forward to its uncocked position.

STEP 50

The claws on the end of the mainspring are hooked over the stirrup as shown.

STEP 51

The mainspring is pushed up against the lockplate with its pin entering its lockplate hole as shown.

STEP 52
The hammer-retaining screw is now replaced and lock reassembly is complete.

BREECHBLOCK REASSEMBLY

STEP 53
The breechblock catch and its spring are slipped into the back of the breechblock, aligned as shown in the picture.

STEP 54
The thumb release is inserted into its slot and the holes lined up.

STEP 55
The screw/pin that retains the thumb release is returned to its place and tightened. This screw/pin is indicated with an arrow in the photograph.

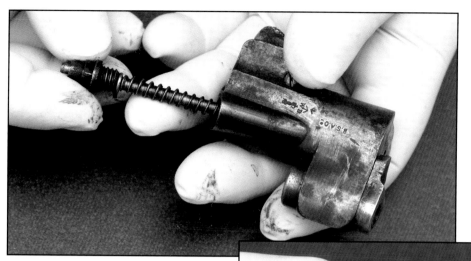

STEP 56

The firing pin, its spring and its retaining nut are slipped into place as shown. The nut is then tightened.

STEP 57

The breechblock is now slid into the breech of the rifle as shown.

STEP 58

The breechblock hinge pin is slid into place. Notice the hole in the pin. This lines up with the corresponding hole in the breech — but it is not pushed in all the way yet.

STEP 59

(left) The extractor spring and its cover are compressed and pushed into place.

(right) The hinge pin is now slipped all the way in, lining up the two holes, and the retaining screw is replaced.

Other steps in rifle reassembly are a reversal of disassembly steps.

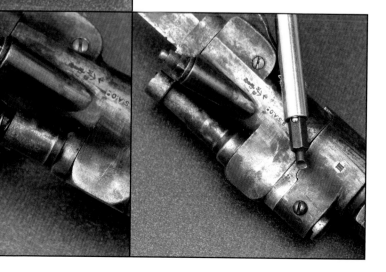

The .45-70 Trapdoor Springfield

STEP 1

After ensuring that the rifle is not loaded, the lock is loosened by placing it at half cock and taking out the two screws shown. It is sometimes helpful to unscrew these screws a few turns and tap them gently with a plastic-headed hammer to start the lock out of its inlet.

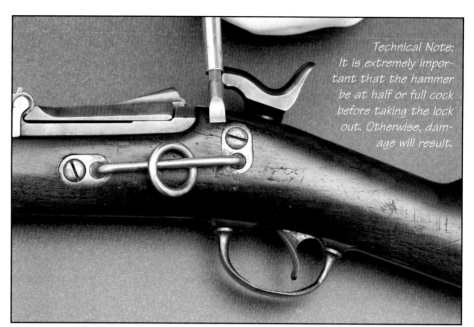

Technical Note: It is extremely important that the hammer be at half or full cock before taking the lock out. Otherwise, damage will result.

STEP 2

The breechblock catch is pushed forward, opening the breech, and the lock carefully removed. It is easy to chip the wood surrounding it. Disassembly of the lock itself will not be covered here. It is essentially identical to the lock disassembly shown in the section on the Snider, so repetition seems unnecessary.

STEP 3

The screw passing through the barrel tang into the triggerguard is removed.

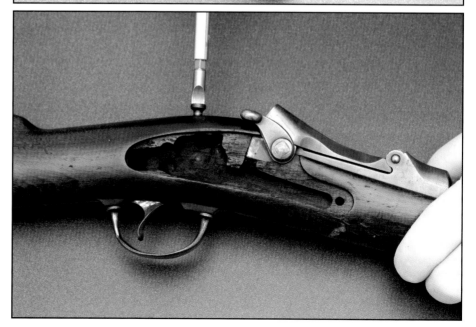

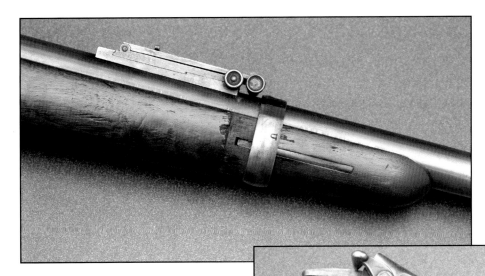

STEP 4
The barrel band spring is depressed and the band slid forward and off the carbine. A rifle would have additional bands to remove.

STEP 5
The barrel and receiver are now lifted out of the stock.

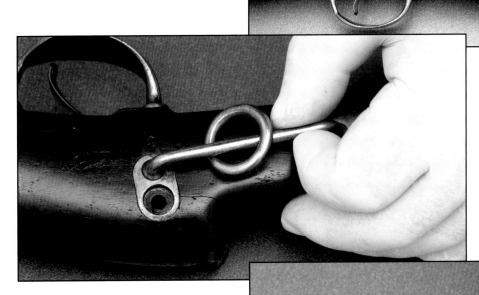

STEP 6
The swivel bar can be removed if necessary, albeit this must be done carefully and risks damaging the wood.

STEP 7
The front and rear trigger-guard screws are taken out.

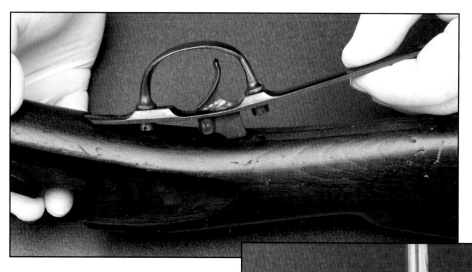

STEP 8

The triggerguard with attached trigger mechanism is lifted out of the stock as shown. Note that it is very easy to chip the wood of the stock while taking out the triggerguard, so this is not done unless absolutely necessary.

STEP 9

The buttplate screws are carefully withdrawn.

STEP 10

Seen here is the inside of the buttplate and the inletting in the wood of the butt itself.

STEP 11

The trigger is retained by split nuts as shown. These can be removed with a special tool if necessary, but we did not do that here.

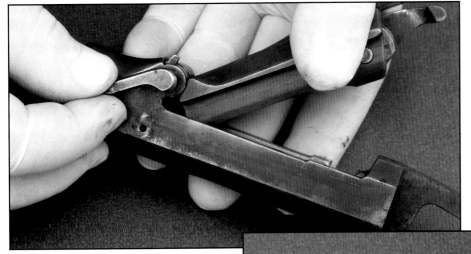

STEP 12

The hinge pin is pulled out of its hole from its lever end.

STEP 13

With the hinge pin removed, the breechblock lifts out and the extractor can be removed.

STEP 14

A spring and detent (the little pointy thing stuck in the end of the spring) are located behind the extractor. These can come out as shown. These are difficult to put back, however, and are left in when at all possible.

STEP 15

(left) The screw retaining the locking lever and cam is removed.

(right) The locking assembly lifts out of the block. Note the cam spring protruding. This falls out.

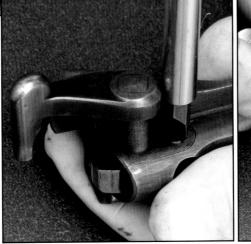

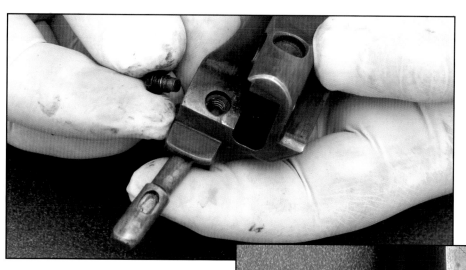

STEP 16

The firing pin retaining screw is removed and the firing pin slipped out. This completes the disassembly.

REASSEMBLY

Reassembly is basically a reversal of disassembly steps. However, if the extractor has been removed, it must be pressed into place (compressing its spring using a thumb). It is held in this position by a drifting punch (coming from the right side of the photo) and the hinge pin reinserted as the punch is withdrawn.

Differences for Rod Bayonet Rifles

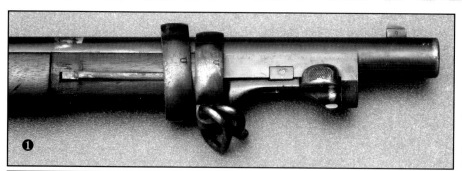

❶

The rod bayonet rifles require a different barrel disassembly procedure. The barrel bands are slid forward. They will not go over the rod bayonet fixture and stay as shown in photo #1. The action is gently tapped with a block of wood until it barely comes free of the stock. The breech is then lifted no more than is shown in photo #3. The stock can then be pulled back away from the rod bayonet fixture.

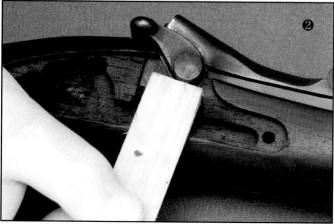

❷

❸

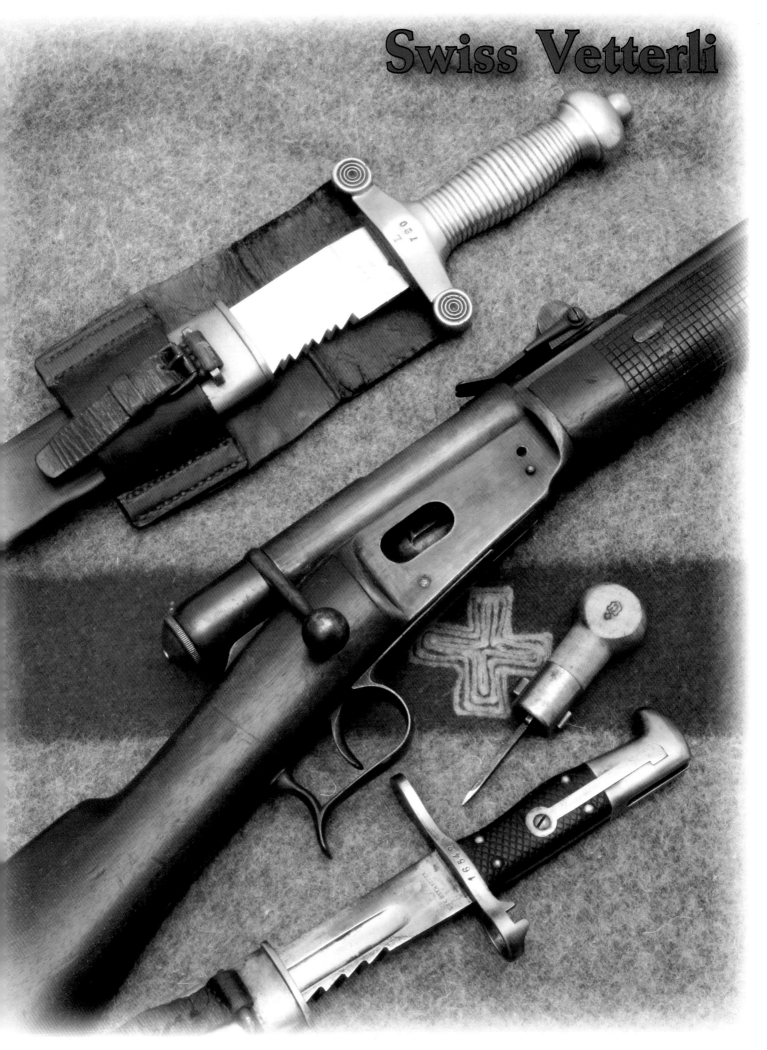

Swiss Vetterli

STEP 1

First, we make sure that the rifle is unloaded. This particular example is a Model 1869/71, but all Swiss Vetterlis, whether rifles, carbines or sharpshooter versions, disassemble similarly.

STEP 2

The bolt-retaining key is pushed out with the blade of a screwdriver. This key does not come completely out. We do not try to remove the bolt at this point, because (perhaps surprisingly) more disassembly is required before this can happen.

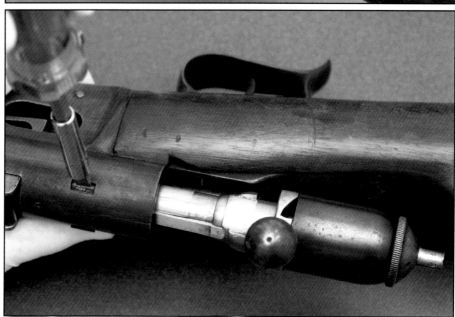

STEP 3

The screw that retains the trigger assembly is removed.

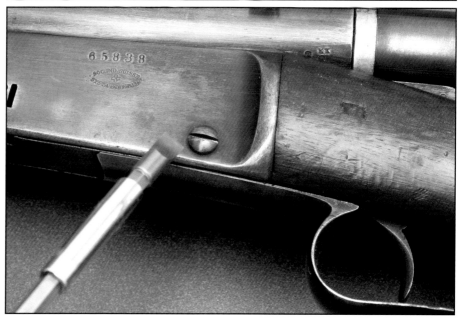

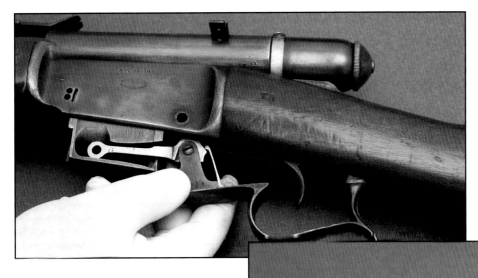

STEP 4

The trigger assembly cartridge riser can now be pulled gently down and out of the rifle.

STEP 5

The bolt is now removed.

STEP 6

(left) After its retaining spring is depressed, the forend cap is removed.

(right) The screws on the two barrel bands are loosened and then they are slid off of the rifle.

STEP 7

(see inset) The barrel-retaining key is driven to the far side. This can require a screwdriver with a particularly long and thin blade. This key does not come completely out.

The forend is now pulled forward and off.

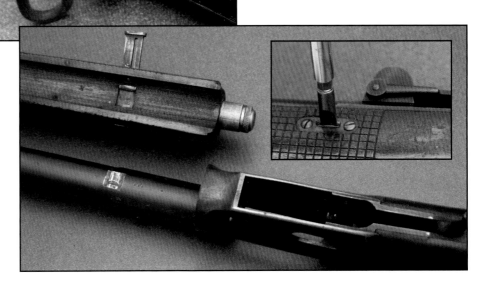

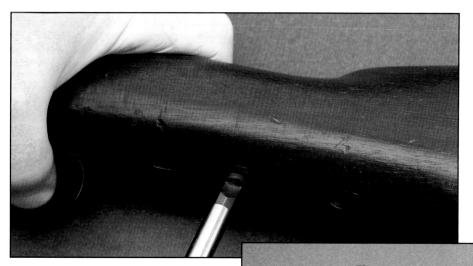

STEP 8

The two screws retaining the triggerguard tang are removed.

STEP 9

The buttstock is now pulled gently to the rear and off. This sometimes requires gentle tapping with a rubber-headed hammer.

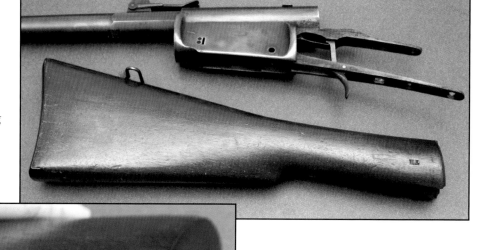

STEP 10

The two buttplate screws are removed. There is usually a compartment drilled out of the wood under the buttplate for holding a spare firing pin.

STEP 11

If necessary, the trigger spring and trigger can be removed by driving out one pin and unscrewing one screw.

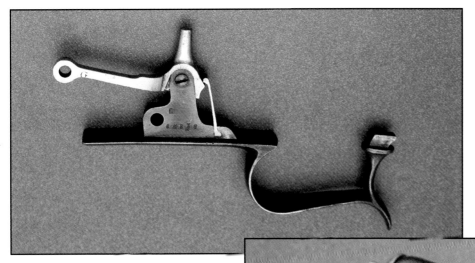

STEP 12

If necessary, the elevator assembly can be disassembled by removing the screw shown here.

REASSEMBLY

Reassembly is a reversal of the disassembly steps, remembering that the bolt must be put into place before the elevator is inserted. This is shown in the photograph at right.

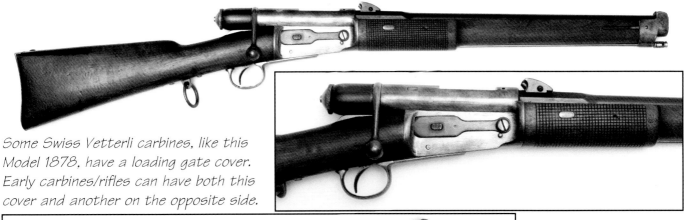

Swiss Vetterlis with Differences

Some Swiss Vetterli carbines, like this Model 1878, have a loading gate cover. Early carbines/rifles can have both this cover and another on the opposite side.

(left) Sharpshooter variations of the Swiss Vetterli, like this Model 1871 Repetierstutzer, have double-set triggers as shown in this photograph.

Swiss Vetterli Bolt

Disassembly:

Disassembling a Vetterli bolt can require lots of hand strength. First, the bolt's knurled spring-retaining nut (at the end of the nose cap) is unscrewed and removed.

With the nut unscrewed, the nose cap and spring are removed and set aside.

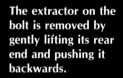

At the end of the bolt head there is a slot retaining the firing pin. This is removed. Note that it has two prongs for rimfire cartridge ignition.

The extractor on the bolt is removed by gently lifting its rear end and pushing it backwards.

Next, the striking pin is slid out and removed. This is the part that is often called a firing pin, but in this case the firing pin is actually a separate piece in the bolt head.

The bolt handle is pulled to the rear and removed.

The disassembled bolt (showing clockwise from upper right corner): Bolt Handle, Spring Retaining Nut, Extractor, Nose Cap, Striker, Firing Pin, Bolt Body and Spring.

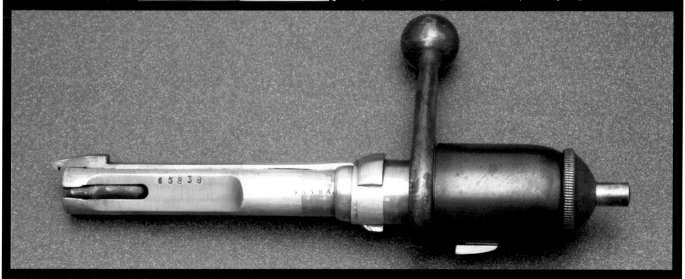

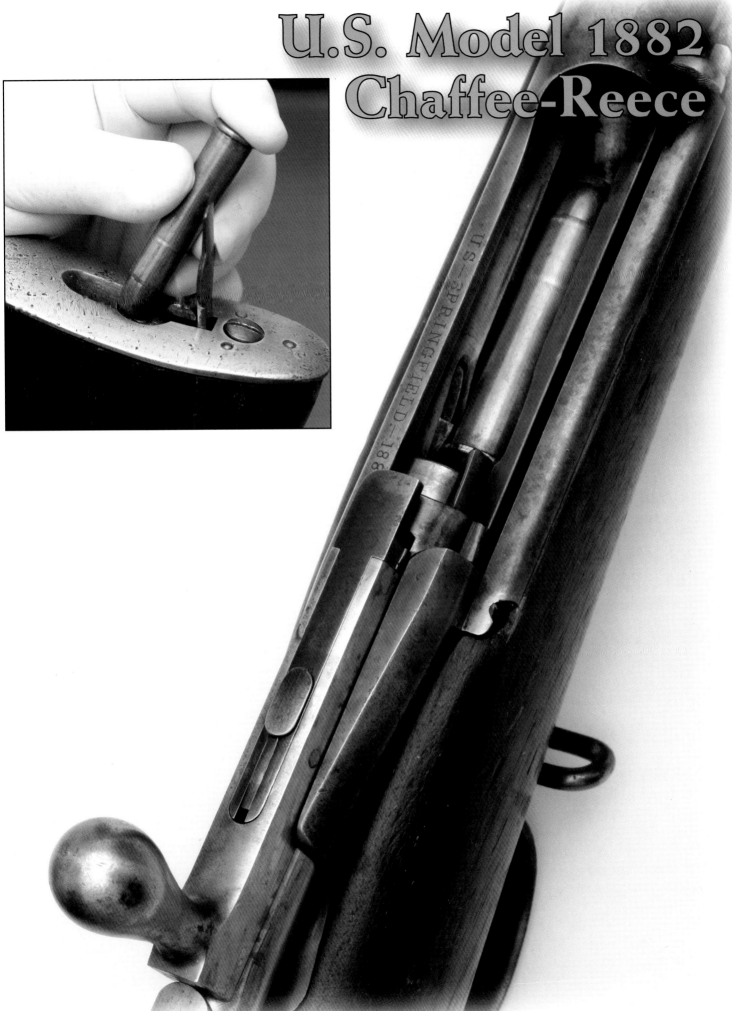

STEP 1

As always, we first confirm that the rifle isn't loaded. To check the magazine in the butt, it is necessary to open the bolt and flip up the loading door in the buttplate.

The magazine is disconnected by pushing the magazine cut-off lever forward to the position shown (see arrow).

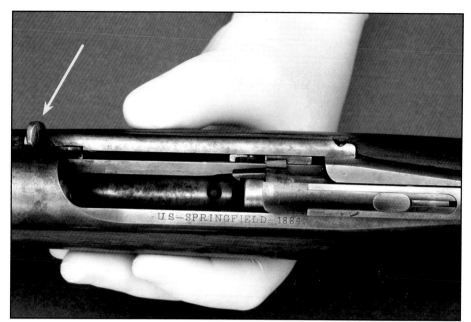

STEP 2

The small lever on the top of the bolt is lifted in order to release the catch that holds the bolt head/extractor in place.

STEP 3

The next step is to remove the bolt head/extractor, but before doing so it is important to check the location of the tiny tab (see arrow at right) on the end of the arm that connects the magazine to the bolt. The tab should be in the position shown.

STEP 4

With the extractor catch open, the bolt head/extractor can be lifted up and off the bolt.

STEP 5

The trigger is now pulled back and the bolt is withdrawn from the rifle.

STEP 6

The front and rear screws are removed from the triggerguard.

STEP 7

The triggerguard is now pulled off, over the trigger.

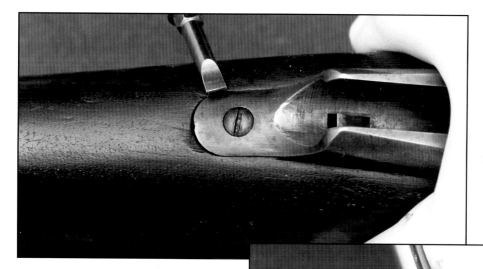

STEP 8
The screw at the back of the receiver is removed.

STEP 9
The two screws holding the buttplate in place are removed.

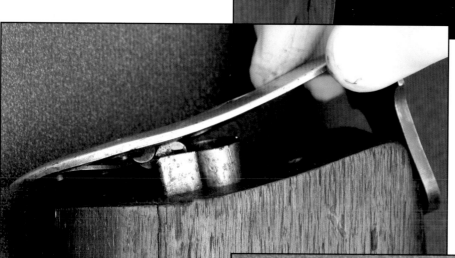

STEP 10
The buttplate is lifted off. Note the way in which it is hooked into the bottom edge of the magazine tube.

STEP 11
The cleaning rod is now taken out.

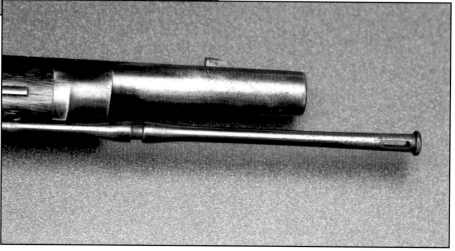

STEP 12

The front barrel band spring is depressed and the band pulled off.

STEP 13

The rear barrel band is removed in the same fashion.

STEP 14

The magazine tube is pulled out about four inches.

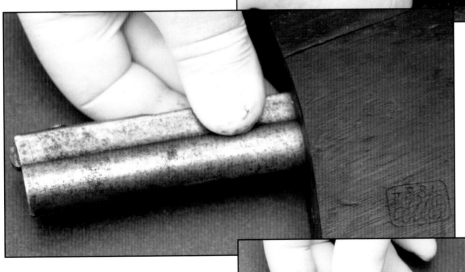

STEP 15

The barrel and receiver can now be lifted and pulled slightly forward in order to free them from the stock.

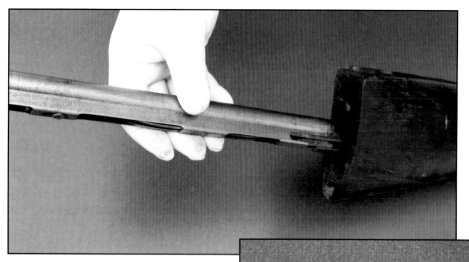

STEP 16

The magazine is fully withdrawn. In order to come out, it must be twisted slightly (as shown in the photo), being careful not to damage the fragile mechanism.

STEP 17

The two screws that hold the plate on the side of the receiver are now taken out.

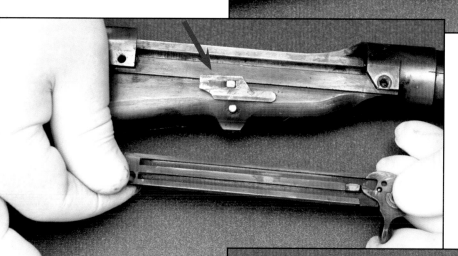

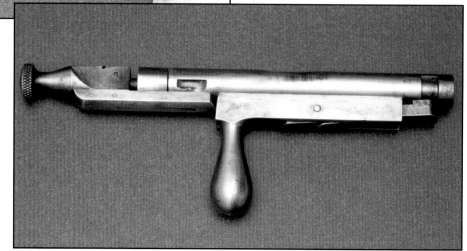

STEP 18

The plate keeps the magazine cut-off in place as well as the sliding piece (see arrow) that connects to the magazine.

STEP 19

The bolt, out of the rifle, with the bolt head/extractor removed.

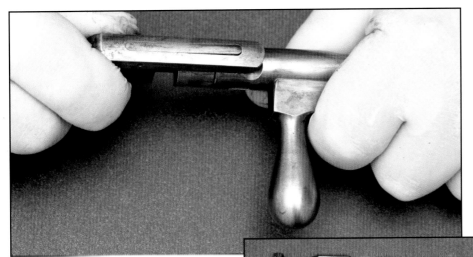

STEP 20

The bolt is disassembled by firmly grasping the cocking piece and rotating it away from the bolt handle while pulling out. The two parts come apart abruptly.

STEP 21

The two main pieces of the bolt assembly. Because everything else is assembled with pins that would have to be drifted out, it was decided not to disassemble it further.

Reassembling the Chaffee-Reece

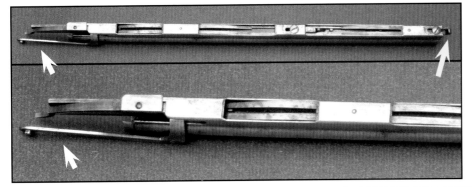

STEP 22

To replace the magazine, the connecting arm (white arrow) is pulled forward as far as it will go, and the projection coming out of the rear of the magazine (yellow arrow) is pulled back as far as it will go, before the magazine is slipped back into the stock.

STEP 23

The magazine is twisted slightly (as shown) in order to start it back into its hole in the stock. It is pushed in so that the connecting arm enters the inlet for the action but the magazine tube does not block the hole for the trigger.

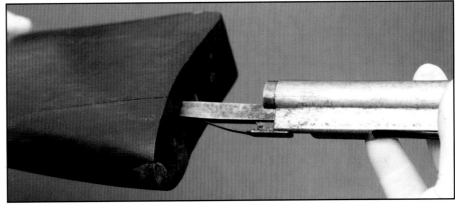

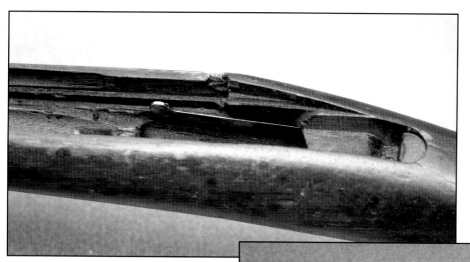

STEP 24

The connecting arm projecting into the inlet. It must rest on the wood as shown in the photo to the left. If it falls further into the inlet, it will be impossible to reconnect all of the parts.

STEP 25

The barreled action is now returned to the stock, taking care not to move the connecting arm and not seating it fully in its inlet.

STEP 26

The magazine tube is now pushed in, taking care to seat its end in the action.

STEP 27

The photo at the right shows the sliding piece (connecting the magazine to the bolt) in place but without its retaining plate. Assembling these small parts is difficult but this is the arrangement we are trying to achieve. The arrow is pointing to the small tab on the end of the magazine connecting arm.

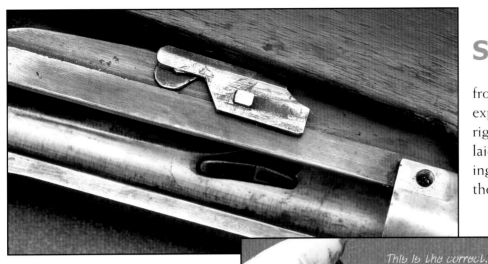

STEP 28

The action is pulled away from the stock just enough to expose the two screw holes on its right side, and the sliding piece is laid over the tab on the connecting arm as shown in the photo at the left.

STEP 29

Holding the magazine cut-off in place (left hand fingers in photo), the retaining plate is turned over and placed on the sliding piece. The tab should slide in the bottom groove.

STEP 30

With these pieces in place, the screws that hold the plate in place are replaced. This is done carefully as everything falls to pieces very easily.

STEP 31

Properly assembled, the parts should look like the photo at the right. The long slot in the sliding piece (see arrow) holds the bolt head/extractor. The position of the tab on the connecting arm can be changed by pushing the sliding piece and must be forward of the long slot or the bolt head/extractor will not go in.

STEP 32

Taking care not to disturb anything, the screw at the end of the action is replaced. Both barrel bands can now be put on (not shown).

STEP 33

The magazine tube is pulled out slightly, the buttplate hooked in place and its screws returned.

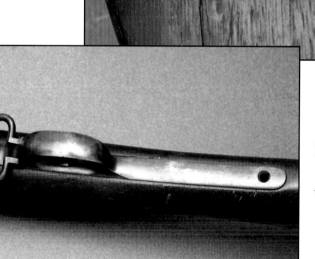

STEP 34

The trigger guard is replaced with its screws at both ends.

STEP 35

The bolt head/extractor. The arrow is pointing to the part that slides down into the long slot in the top of the sliding piece. When properly in place, the notch aligns with the tab on the magazine connecting arm.

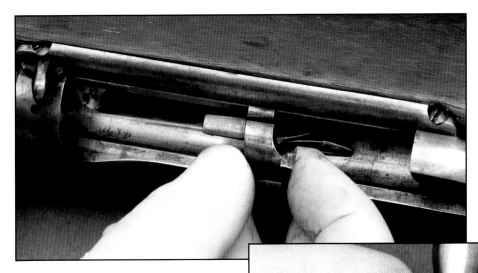

STEP 36

The bolt head/extractor is now slipped into the slot in the sliding piece.

STEP 37

The bolt is reassembled by sliding the two pieces together as shown in the photo at the right. The cocking piece is turned towards the bolt handle.

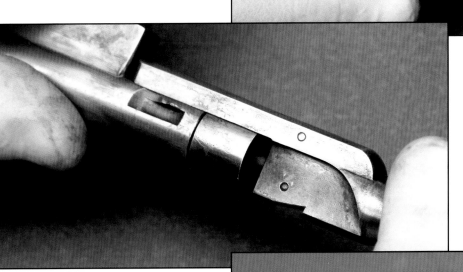

STEP 38

When the cocking piece stops, it is pulled out and turned further to the fully cocked position shown in the photo on the left.

STEP 39

Holding back the trigger, the bolt is slipped into the action.

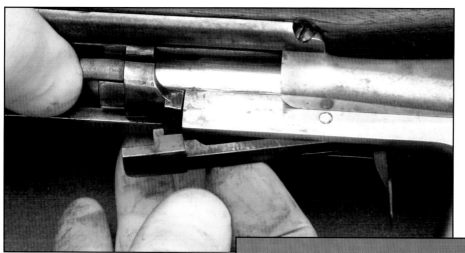

STEP 40

The bolt head/extractor is now wiggled into place and the lever, which keeps its retaining catch in place, pushed back down.

STEP 41

Reassembled, the Chaffee-Reece action looks like this. It is easy to appreciate why the Army rejected this design.

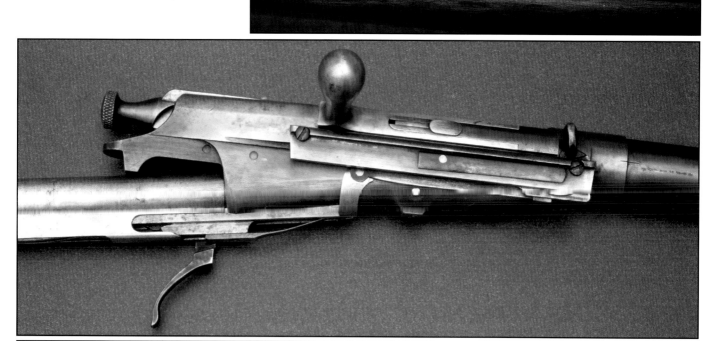

U.S.-SPRINGFIELD.-1884.

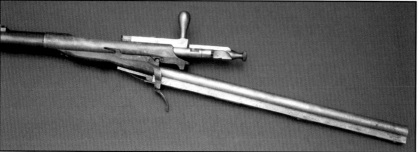

BONUS PHOTOS

We were going to leave the bottom of this page blank, but then said, "What the heck, let's show some more views of the gun!" No one ever complained that there were too many photos of guns in a gun book. So here you go.

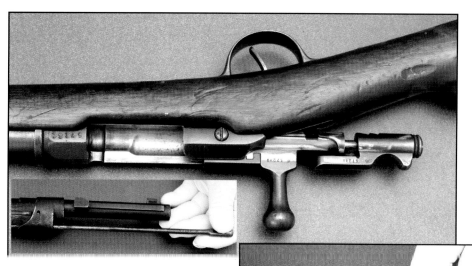

STEP 1

The rifle chosen for disassembly is a Gras Model 1874/80/14. As always, before beginning, we keep the rifle pointed in a safe direction and check that it is not loaded. Then, the cleaning rod is unscrewed, withdrawn and set aside.

STEP 2

The bolt retaining screw (see arrow) is removed, and with the trigger pulled, the bolt is slid out of the action.

STEP 3

The nose cap and barrel band are removed by depressing their retaining springs and pulling them forward and off the rifle. Some Gras rifles have handguards. In these cases, the handguard would come off at this point.

STEP 4

The screw at the receiver tang is removed.

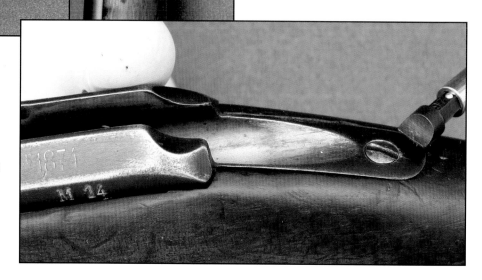

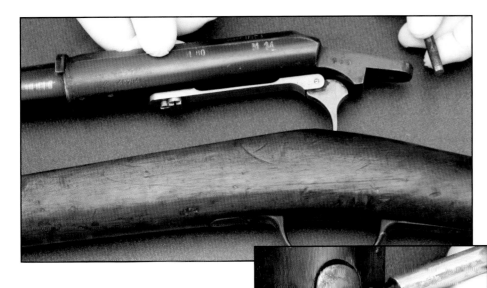

STEP 5

The barreled action is lifted out of the stock.

STEP 6

The two wood screws retaining the triggerguard are taken out and the triggerguard itself lifted out of the rifle.

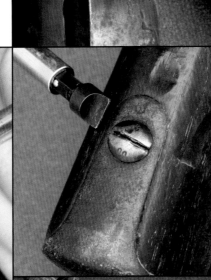

STEP 7

The rear sling swivel and the buttplate can be removed by taking out their respective screws (two each).

STEP 8

To remove the trigger assembly, first, the set screw is removed as shown in the main photo at the right. Then the square-headed screw (see top inset photo) is taken out. This allows the trigger and its spring to be lifted out of the receiver (see lower inset).

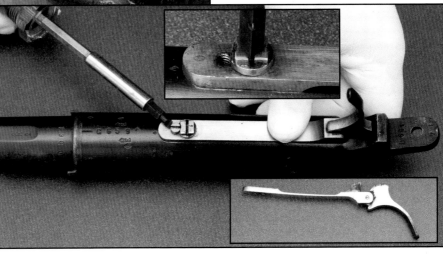

The Gras Bolt

Disassembly:

The Gras bolt as removed from the rifle. The multiple serial numbers are a result of this rifle having been rebuilt several times.

The bolt head is removed by turning it 1/4 turn (as shown at the right) and pulling it off.

The extractor is removed, compressing it slightly with the fingers and pulling it out of the bolt head.

The cocking piece is rotated 1/4 turn in order to relieve pressure on the mainspring.

The knurled cap is turned so that its slot aligns with the mark on the cocking piece (see inset). With the tip of the firing pin against a block of wood, the cocking piece is pushed down and the cap slid off.

With the knurled cap removed, all of the bolt components come apart readily.

knurled cap

cocking piece

bolt head and extractor

bolt body

firing pin/striker with mainspring

Reassembly:

The mainspring is slipped over the firing pin's striker and both parts are slid into the bolt body.

The cocking piece is slipped over the end of the firing pin/striker as shown in the photo at the right.

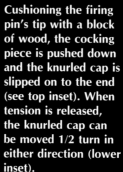

Cushioning the firing pin's tip with a block of wood, the cocking piece is pushed down and the knurled cap is slipped on to the end (see top inset). When tension is released, the knurled cap can be moved 1/2 turn in either direction (lower inset).

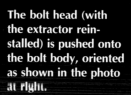

The bolt head (with the extractor reinstalled) is pushed onto the bolt body, oriented as shown in the photo at right.

When it is seated against the bolt body, the bolt head is rotated 1/4 turn so that it aligns with the bolt handle.

The cocking piece is now pulled back and the bolt returned to the cocked position. It is then returned to the rifle.

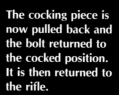

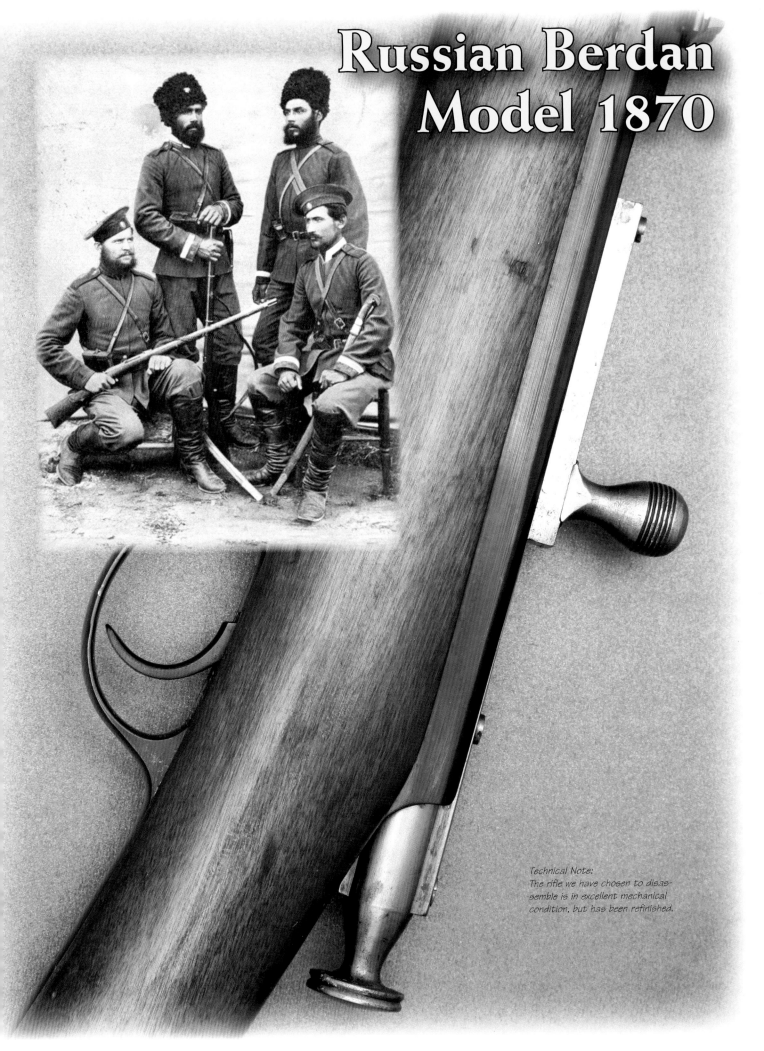

Russian Berdan
Model 1870

Technical Note:
The rifle we have chosen to disassemble is in excellent mechanical condition, but has been refinished.

STEP 1

With the muzzle pointed in a safe direction, the bolt is opened and it is confirmed that the rifle isn't loaded.

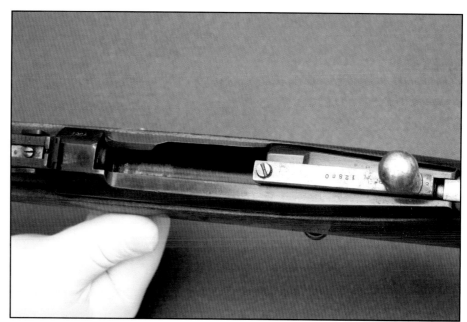

STEP 2

(top) The cleaning rod is removed.

(bottom) The bolt is removed by drawing it back and depressing the sear (see arrow) with a screwdriver blade. The bolt can then be drawn out to the rear.

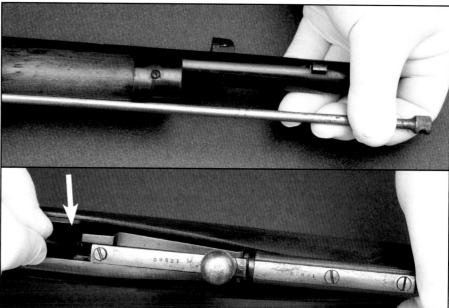

STEP 3

(left photo) The front barrel band is loosened. Note that the retaining screws are captured and that pressure is relieved by screwing them in, not out.

(center photo) The front barrel band is slipped off the rifle.

(right photo) The rear barrel band is loosened and removed.

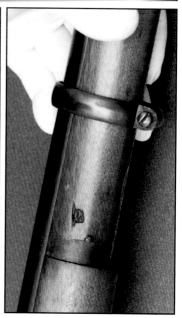

STEP 4

The screw at the rear of the action is removed.

STEP 5

The barrel and receiver can now be lifted out of the stock.

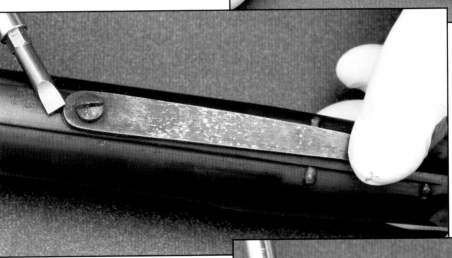

STEP 6

A single screw retains the combination trigger and sear spring.

STEP 7

(left photo) The triggerguard is removed by taking out the wood screws holding it at either end.

(right photo) The buttplate is retained by two screws and can be taken out if desired. Reassembly is a simple reversal of disassembly steps.

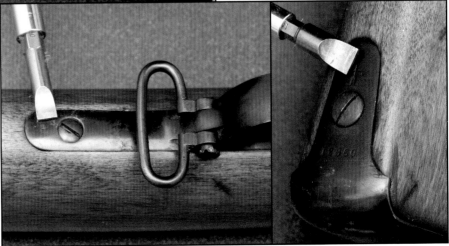

Berdan II Bolt

Disassembly:

The two screws in the rear half of the bolt are removed. The front screw is very short while the rear screw includes a pin that passes through the firing pin.

The rear half of the bolt is now unscrewed from the forward half and set aside.

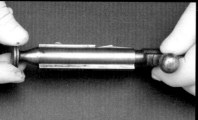

The extractor is removed by taking out its retaining pin. Note that it must be kept under pressure to prevent it from springing out.

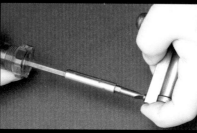

The pin/screw just behind the bolt head is now removed. This will release the bolt head, which must be held in (see index finger) as it is under pressure of the mainspring.

With the screw/pin removed, the bolt head, mainspring and firing pin will come out. Care is taken because the spring is under pressure.

The bolt head, mainspring and firing pin come apart easily. The bolt is now disassembled as shown.

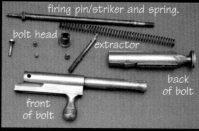

firing pin/striker and spring.
bolt head
extractor
front of bolt
back of bolt

Reassembly:

The mainspring and bolt head are slipped onto the firing pin and pushed into the bolt body so that the screw/pin hole aligns as shown. The screw is returned to its place.

The extractor and its spring are slipped into place, oriented as shown. (See flat spot indicated by arrow.)

Using the index finger to hold the extractor and its spring in place, the retaining screw is replaced to hold it all together.

The rear half of the bolt is screwed onto the firing pin. This action is complete when you can see through the rear hole and out the other side of the bolt. The screws are then returned to place.

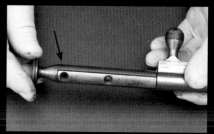

In order to insert the assembled bolt into the rifle, the front half is slipped into place and the rear half rotated slightly until it is oriented as shown. The bolt then slides forward.

Interestingly, the bolt head does not contact the rear of the barrel. See area indicated by the arrow.

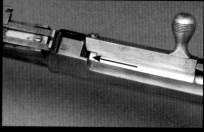

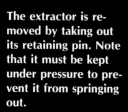

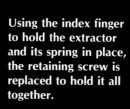

Mauser Model 1871
and 1871/84

STEP 1

Since the Model 71/84 is the most commonly encountered version of this rifle, it has been chosen for disassembly here. Differences noted for the single-shot Model 1871 will be handled later.

Before disassembly, it is ensured that the rifle and its tubular magazine are unloaded.

STEP 2

The bolt retaining screw is loosened approximately 3.5 turns until it stops rotating. It is not removed.

The thick washer under the bolt retaining screw is pulled up as shown.

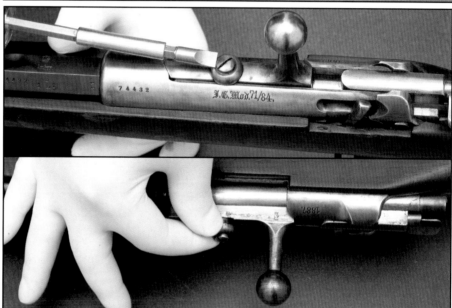

STEP 3

The washer should clear the top of the action. In some cases, it is necessary to pull the bolt sharply back in order to raise the cartridge elevator (see arrow). The bolt cannot be removed if the elevator is not in its upmost position.

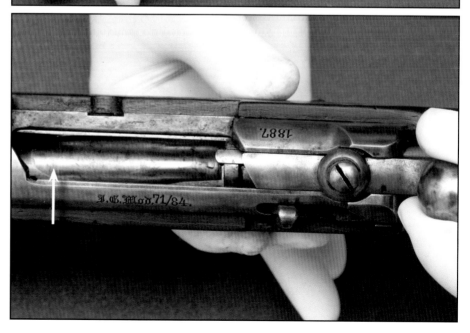

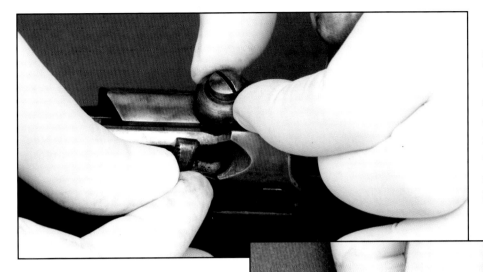

STEP 4

Holding the washer up to clear the action, the magazine cut-off lever (see bottom set of fingers) is pushed slightly towards the rear of the rifle until the bolt is able to slip out of the action. The bolt is now set aside.

STEP 5

The cap on the end of the magazine tube is unscrewed.

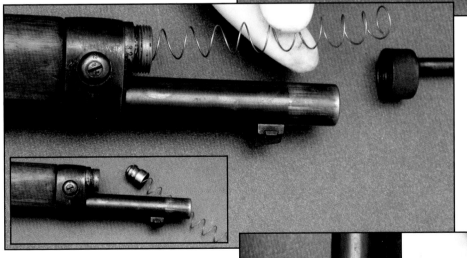

STEP 6

The magazine spring is now carefully pulled out. If it had resisted at all, we would not have choosen to remove it. It is a very light and fragile spring. The end has a cute fixture as shown in the inset photo.

STEP 7

(left) The screw retaining the nosecap key is removed. It is the tiny slot in the middle.

(center) The key is lifted out as shown.

(right) The nosecap is slipped off of the rifle.

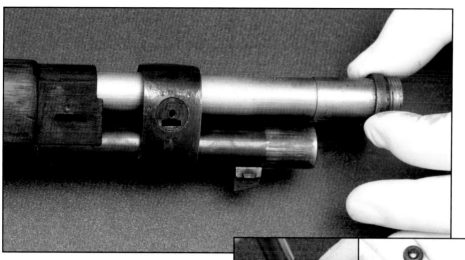

STEP 8

The magazine tube is slipped out. This tube is made of very thin metal and had it stuck at all, we would not have continued removing it. In order to remove the action/barrel, however, it is necessary to at least shift it an inch or two out as shown.

STEP 9

(left) The screw clamping the center barrel band is loosened.

(center) The retaining nut came off and the screw was removed, followed by the swivel.

(right) The band was spread using a screw driver so that it passed over the pin in the stock (see arrow).

STEP 10

The rear barrel band was removed by compressing its spring and sliding the band forward.

STEP 11

(left) The screw on the underside of the rifle, in front of the triggerguard, is removed.

(right) The screw at the rear of the action is also removed.

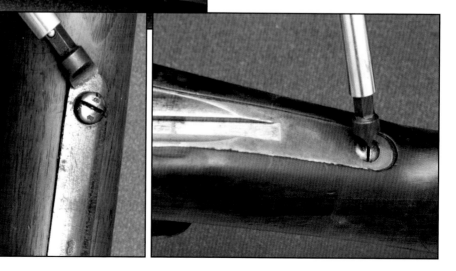

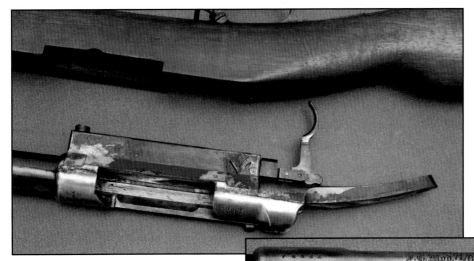

STEP 12

The barreled action was then removed from the stock. A few gentle raps with a plastic hammer were necessary.

STEP 21

The action can be further disassembled, but in this case it did not seem necessary or prudent.

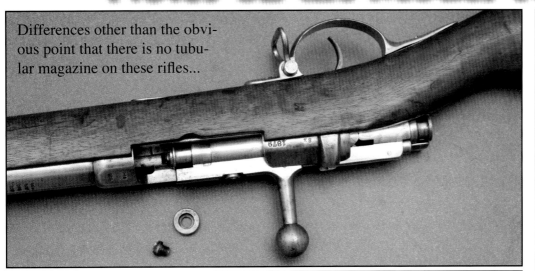

Notes on the Model 1871

Differences other than the obvious point that there is no tubular magazine on these rifles...

On the single shot version of the rifle, the Model 1871, the bolt retaining screw and washer come all the way out (see above). Also, in order to remove the bolt, the trigger must be pulled (see right).

The bolt of the M1871 has an extractor but not an ejector. The Model 71/84, by comparison, has both.

Mauser 71/84 Bolt

Disassembly:

The ejector is lifted off the side of the bolt. There are two little spring clips at the front, but they release quite easily.

The cocking piece is moved one-quarter turn counter-clockwise to relieve tension on the spring and the bolt head is pulled off. The extractor was not removed from the bolt head.

With the tip of the firing pin pressed against a wooden block and downward tension placed on the safety as shown, the firing pin nut is unscrewed.

When the nut comes off the firing pin, all of the bolt components easily come apart at one time.

The dissassembled parts of the Model 71/84 bolt.

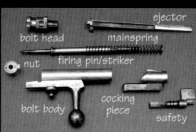

bolt head   ejector   mainspring   nut   firing pin/striker   bolt body   cocking piece   safety

Reassembly:

The flat portion milled on the end of the firing pin is noted for use in the next step.

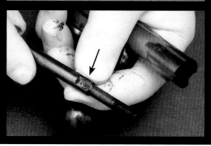

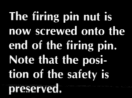

The mainspring is slipped over the firing pin and the two parts slid into the bolt body with the flat (see arrow) oriented as shown in the inset photo.

The tip of the mainspring is pressed against the wooden block and compressed until the flat portion projects from the end of the bolt body. The cocking piece is returned as shown.

The safety is now returned to its slot and held in the position shown while also being compressed.

The firing pin nut is now screwed onto the end of the firing pin. Note that the position of the safety is preserved.

With the bolt parts arranged as shown here, the bolt head is pressed into the bolt body with the extractor slot lined up with the rectangular projection on the cocking piece (see arrows).

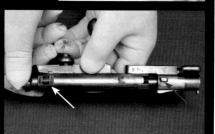

The ejector is now snapped onto the bolt, and the bolt is ready to return to the rifle.

The Model 1886
Portuguese Kropatschek

STEP 1

The Kropatschek is very similar to the M1871/84 Mauser, although there are some distinctive differences.

Needless to say, with the rifle pointed in a safe direction, we first check to make sure that the chamber and magazine are empty.

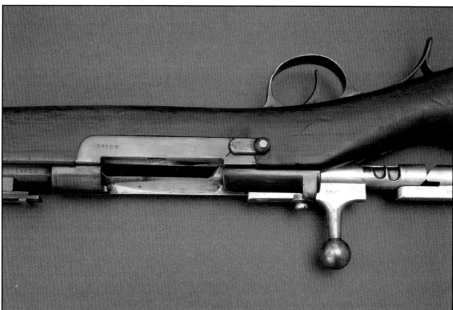

STEP 2

The screw on the bolt stop washer is removed. Unlike the screw on the 71/84 Mauser, it can be taken out and the washer lifted off of the rifle.

STEP 3

The open bolt is now removed by holding the trigger back and withdrawing it from the rifle. On this example, the bolt did not readily stay cocked and it was necessary to hold onto the cocking piece to keep it from snapping into the "fired" position as soon as it cleared the receiver. This is a common fault of these rifles.

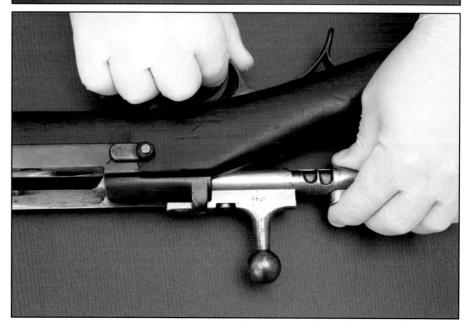

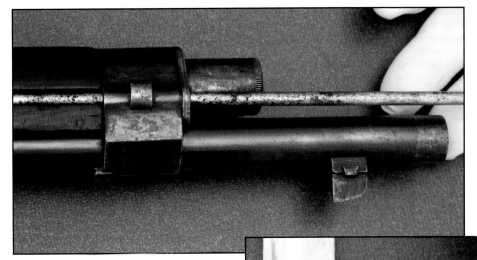

STEP 4
The cleaning rod is now unscrewed and pulled out of the rifle.

STEP 5
The wedge that retains the nosecap is removed by driving it through from the side with the little groove in it.

STEP 6
The magazine cap is removed by turning it with a screwdriver so that the notch on the underside of the cap clears the small lug on the barrel. This is impossible to photograph, but is clear when looking at the rifle.

STEP 7
The magazine spring is now withdrawn. This Slinky®-like spring is very light and fragile, so it is essential that it be handled gently.

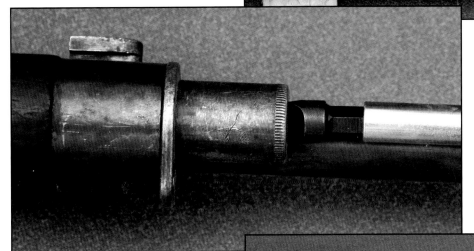

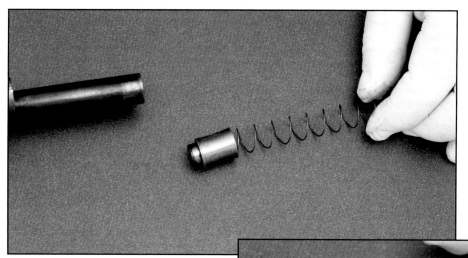

STEP 8

Here we see the plunger at the end of the magazine spring. On this rifle, it was slightly stuck and had it not come free with minimal pressure, we would have left it in place for fear of stretching the spring.

STEP 9

Once the magazine cap has been removed, the nosecap can be slipped off over the front sight.

STEP 10

The two barrel bands are removed by loosening their screws (they do not come all the way out) and slipping them forward and over the front sight.

STEP 11

The screw at the front of the triggerguard is removed. The rear of the triggerguard is secured with a wood screw, which can also be removed at this time, and the guard is gently pulled away from the rifle.

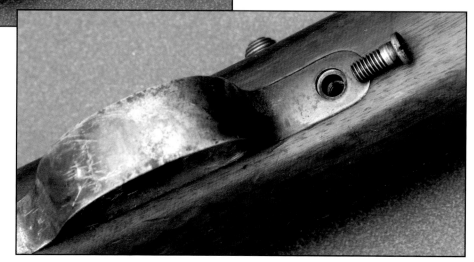

STEP 12

The screw passing through the rear of the tang is now taken out.

STEP 13

In order to remove the action from the stock, it is necessary to pull the magazine tube forward at least a few inches. The tube is often stuck, as was the case here. We made an improvised tool as shown. Inside the tube, the washers expanded and gripped the tube, allowing it to be pulled free.

STEP 14

The action is now free from the stock. Once the magazine tube was pulled forward, it practically jumped from the rifle. It is clear that further dissassembly is possible, but we felt it wasn't necessary in this case. The rotating switch (see arrow) is the magazine cut-off control.

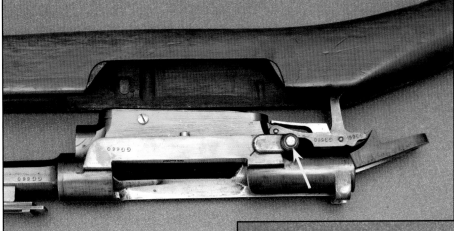

STEP 15

The left side of the Kropatschek action. Note the Model designation and Steyr markings.

The Kropatschek Bolt

Disassembly:

The bolt as it comes out of the rifle. In this case, the bolt slipped into its uncocked position as soon as it was free of the receiver.

The bolt head slips out of the bolt body easily and the extractor (see inset) is also easily taken out.

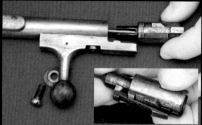

The nut on the end of the firing pin's striker is unscrewed. The spring-loaded safety engages a small notch in the nut and must be depressed in order for the nut to rotate.

When the nut comes off, all of the bolt components come apart easily. In this case, they were tight and it was necessary to give the end of the striker a light tap.

The disassembled parts of the Kropatschek bolt, with the exception of the bolt head and extractor.

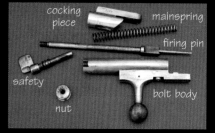

cocking piece

mainspring

firing pin

safety

nut

bolt body

Reassembly:

The flat portion milled on the end of the firing pin/striker is noted for use in the next step.

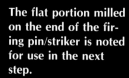

The mainspring is slipped over the firing pin and the two parts slid into the bolt body with the flat facing the long groove (see arrow) in the bolt body.

The tip of the mainspring is pressed against a wood block while the cocking piece and safety are replaced. The flat on the striker aligns with the flat on the inside of the cocking piece.

With the safety and its spring compressed, the nut on the end of the firing pin/striker is screwed on.

The bolt head is slipped over the firing pin in the position shown in the photo at the right.

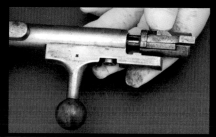

The cocking piece is turned towards the bolt handle, cocking the bolt. In this case, it did not want to stay in this position and had to be held in place while being returned to the receiver.

With the trigger held back and the magazine cut-off in the position shown (see arrow), the bolt slides into the receiver. The bolt stop washer and screw are now replaced.

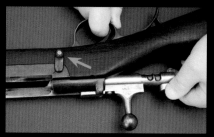

Dutch Model 1871/88
Beaumont Vitali

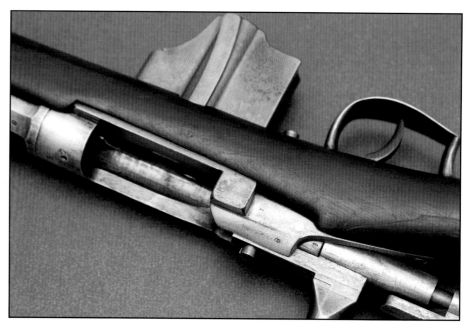

STEP 1

First, it is ensured that the rifle is not loaded and that its Vitali magazine is empty.

STEP 2

The bolt retaining screw is either removed or loosened to its last thread.

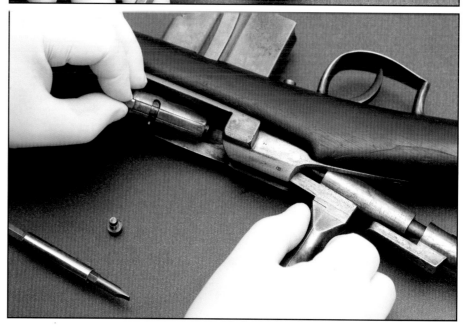

STEP 3

The front half of the bolt is lifted out of the receiver while the rear half is drawn backwards by its handle and out of the rifle.

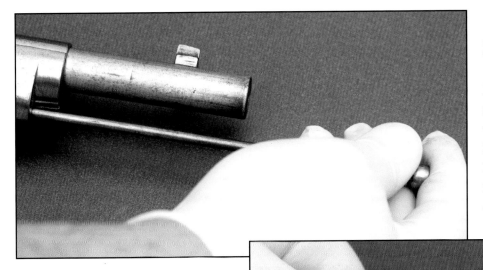

STEP 4

The cleaning rod is removed. Note that Beaumont cleaning rods are missing on almost all rifles that were imported into the United States as surplus during the mid-20th century. Original cleaning rods are usually serial numbered and are highly sought after.

STEP 5

The nose cap retaining spring is depressed and the nose cap is drawn towards the front sight.

STEP 6

The nose cap has to be flipped upside down in order to clear the front sight.

STEP 7

The barrel band retaining spring is depressed and the barrel band slid forward and off the rifle.

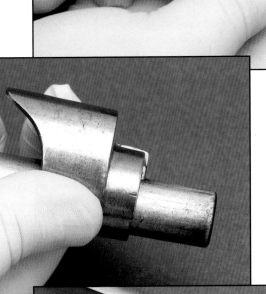

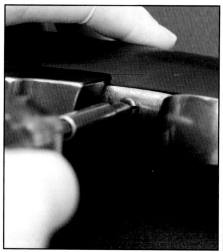

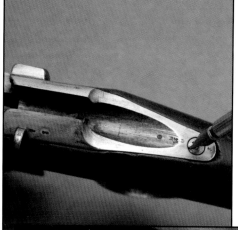

STEP 8

The screw between the magazine and the triggerguard is removed. Then the screw at the back of the action is taken out.

STEP 9

The barreled action can then be lifted out of the stock.

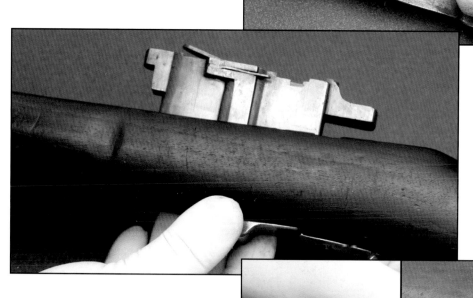

STEP 10

The magazine is pushed up through the top of the stock and out of the rifle.

STEP 11

The screw at the back of the triggerguard is taken out to remove the triggerguard. The sling swivel can be removed by taking out two screws, as can the buttplate. Note that on these Dutch rifles there are generally unit markings on the buttplate tang.

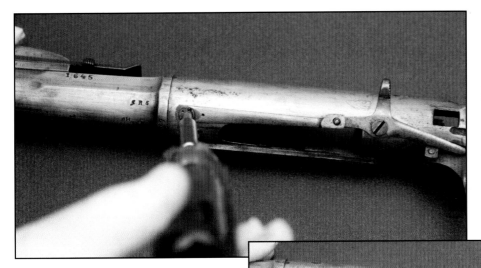

STEP 12

The screw shown here is removed. This is the magazine cut-off assembly.

STEP 13

Next, the screw at the center of the magazine cut-off assembly is taken out.

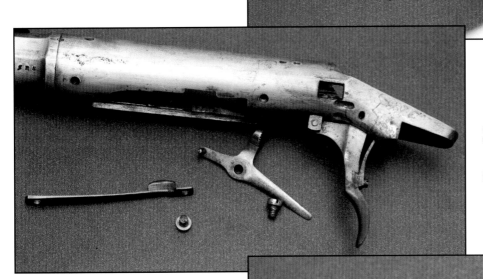

STEP 14

The pieces shown now come free.

STEP 15

All that remains is the trigger assembly. On this rifle, the screws were delicate, so we stopped the disassembly here. But on other rifles, this would be done by taking out the two screws and one pin shown in the photo.

Dutch Beaumont Bolt

Disassembly:

This is what the bolt looks like after it has been taken out of the rifle as described in the steps discussed previously.

The guide (see right hand) is lifted off of the bolt head.

The extractor is dovetailed into the bolt head (see arrow). Unless broken, it should not be removed.

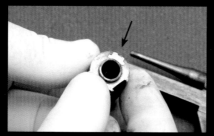

The cocking piece is turned 90 degrees to the left (until it stops) to relieve tension on the striker spring. In the photo, this is being done with the bottom hand.

Holding the two halves of the bolt handle firmly (squeezing), the screw is removed. The handle will come apart under pressure.

This is what the bolt handle looks like when it opens up. The unattached half of the bolt handle and the striker spring can now be removed.

The cocking piece is withdrawn.

This is what the bolt looks like when disassembled. The Beaumont bolt is unique and quite interesting. Note the striker pin does not come out except with a special armorer's tool.

bolt head — firing pin — guide — spring — bolt body — cocking piece — half of bolt handle

Reassembly Notes:

Reassembly is basically a reversal of disassembly. The cocking piece is replaced in the bolt body as shown.

The striker spring and the loose half of the bolt handle are replaced as shown and then screwed together. Note that the long end of the spring goes into the bottom of the handle (see photo).

The bolt head guide is slipped onto the bolt head.

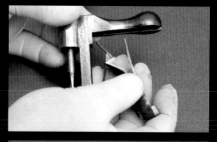

The bolt is assembled in the rifle. The bolt head goes in first, and the back of the bolt slid in to meet it. Then the tip of the retaining screw goes into the slot in the bolt head as shown, holding it together.

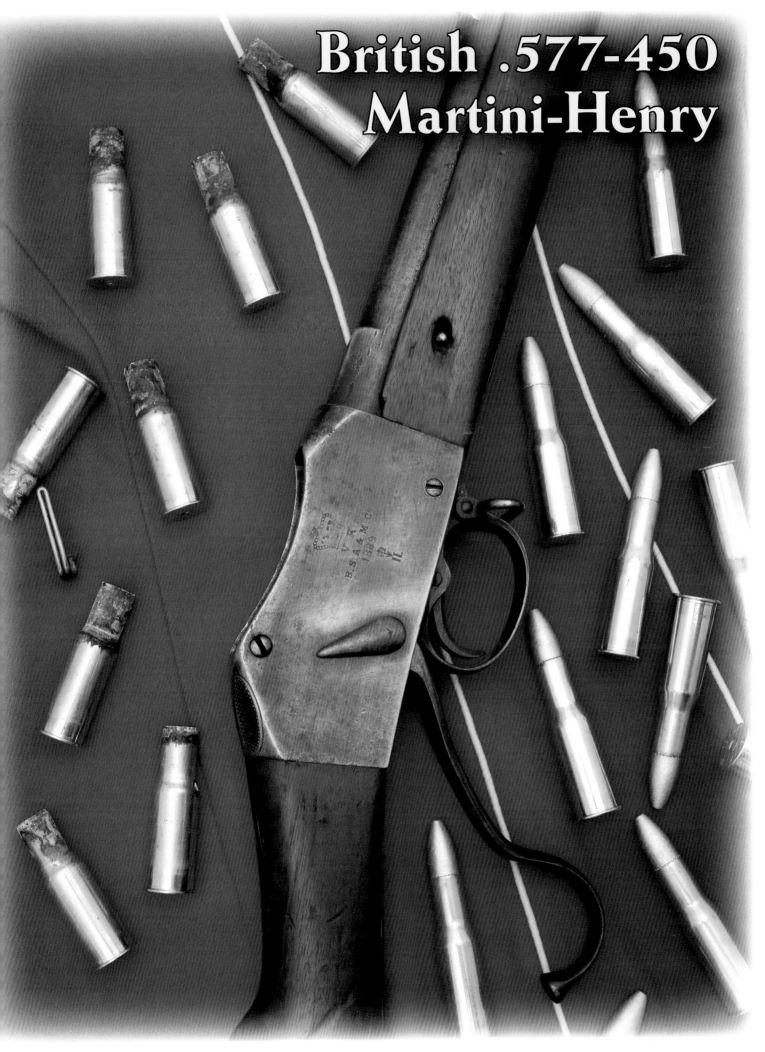

British .577-450
Martini-Henry

STEP 1

First, it is ensured that the rifle is not loaded.

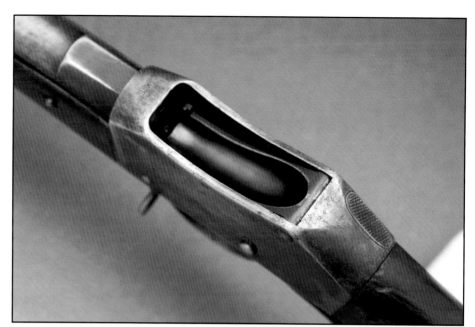

STEP 2

The cleaning rod is removed.

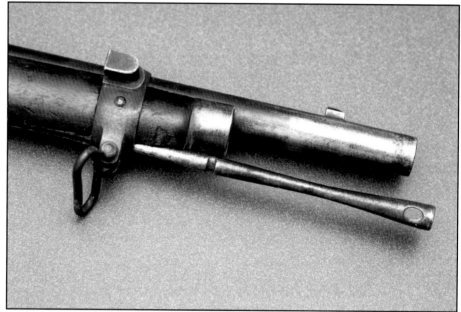

STEP 3

The pin through the front barrel band is driven out.

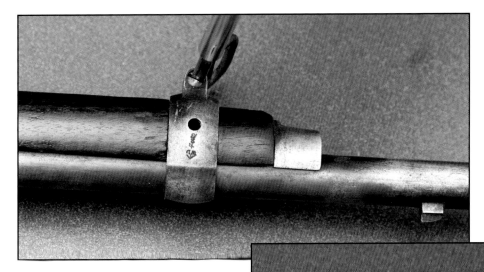

STEP 4

The screw that tightens the front barrel band is loosened. It does not come out.

STEP 5

The front barrel band is slid off of the rifle and set aside.

STEP 6

The rear barrel band screw is loosened. There may also be a pin retaining this piece that needs to be driven out.

STEP 7

The rear barrel band is slid off the rifle and set aside.

STEP 8

The pin at the rear of the fore-stock is driven out.

STEP 9

The forestock is now taken off by pulling it straight down.

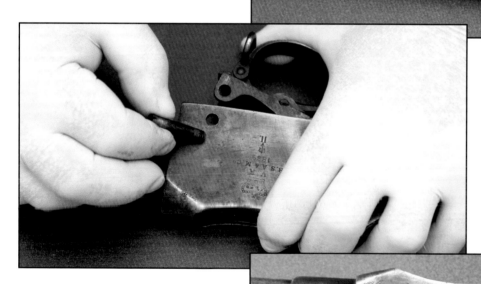

STEP 10

The screw at the bottom front of the action is removed. It only has a few threads and must be pushed out the rest of the way once it is loosened.

STEP 11

The locking screw is taken out as shown.

STEP 12

The pin/cocking indicator can now be pushed in the direction of its larger side and pulled out.

STEP 13

The trigger assembly and cocking lever can now be pulled out of the rifle.

STEP 14

The extractor (left) and tumbler (right) will now fall out.

STEP 15

The pin at the top rear of the action is driven out. Note that this looks like a screw, but it is not. It is driven out from the slotted end. Trying to drive it out from the other direction will cause damage.

STEP 16
The rear sling swivel is removed by withdrawing its screw.

STEP 17
The trigger spring screw is removed.

STEP 18
The trigger spring now comes free.

STEP 19
The trigger screw is taken out.

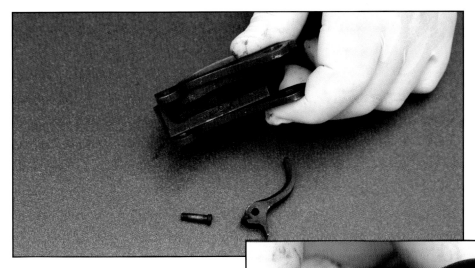

STEP 20
The trigger slides out and the trigger assembly is now disassembled.

STEP 21
The breechblock is often left assembled, but can be taken to pieces by removing the locking screw (already taken out here). The mainspring is removed by unscrewing the large retaining collar seen here.

Reassembling the Martini Action

STEP 22
With the trigger assembly reassembled, the lever, trigger assembly and extractor are arranged as shown and pushed up into the frame. The front screw is inserted to keep the parts in place.

STEP 23
The tumbler goes back into the action oriented as shown. The square shaft of the cocking indicator passes through the hole.

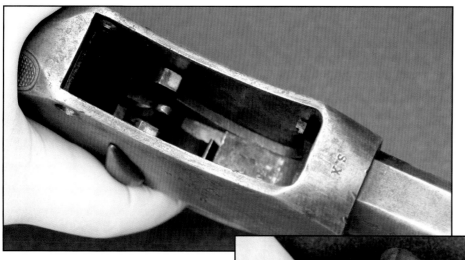

STEP 24

When assembled correctly, the cocking indicator, tumbler and the projecting ears of the lever should appear as in the photo.

STEP 25

The trigger is pushed forward and the lever slightly lowered so that the three projecting pieces are nearly vertical, without allowing the sear to slip off the trigger. The breech block is then inserted front end down, and the rear pushed down so that the ears of the lever and tumbler engage the

block. This can be difficult and will often require considerable effort. When the parts do engage, they snap into place.

If the three pieces are arranged as seen on the left, they are in the wrong position and the breechblock will not go in.

STEP 26

The split pin can now be returned to the action. It enters from the cocking indicator side. With the block in place, it should easily snap in.

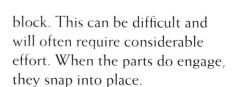

German Gew. 1888 "Commission" Rifle

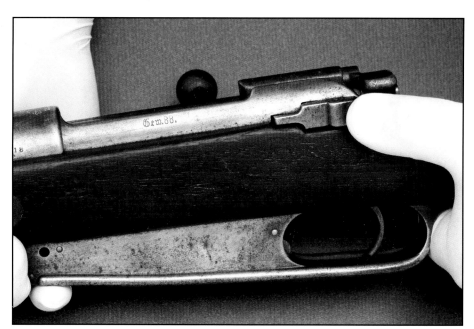

STEP 1

Having made sure that the rifle is not loaded, the bolt release on the left side of the receiver is pressed in.

STEP 2

With the release pushed in, the bolt is then turned up and pulled straight back.

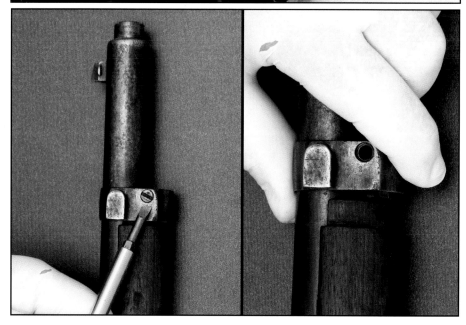

STEP 3

(left photo) The screw that passes through the front barrel band is then removed.

(right photo) The band is pushed forward to remove it. This may be difficult, as they are often stuck. Gentle tapping on the bayonet lug with a plastic-headed hammer is sometimes required.

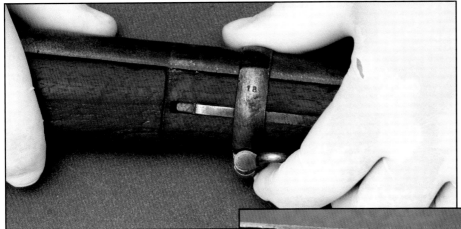

STEP 4

The center barrel band spring is then depressed, and the band slid forward off the stock.

STEP 5

Next, the screw at the rear of the magazine/trigger guard is removed. It is important to use a proper fitting screwdriver. Note: although not present on this rifle, some Gew. 88s have an additional tiny screw that serves to lock the magazine/trigger guard screws in place. When encountered, these are removed first.

STEP 6

The front screw is then removed from the magazine.

STEP 7

It should now be possible to pull the magazine/triggerguard out of the stock. This must be done very carefully as it is often stuck solid with old grease/dirt. Again, gentle tapping with a plastic-headed hammer was necessary, being careful not to damage the sides of the stock inlet.

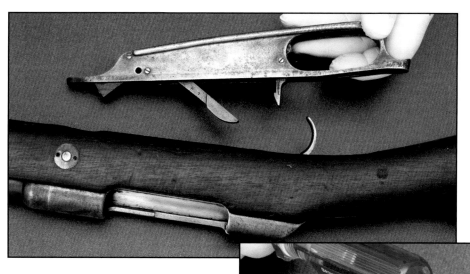

STEP 8

The magazine/trigger guard removed. At this point, nothing is retaining the receiver, although it may be effectively glued in with old, hardened grease.

STEP 9

In this case, the receiver did not simply fall out. The front magazine screw was replaced and its head was tapped with the plastic screwdriver handle, carefully and gently. It is inadvisable to pull the barrel and stock apart from the muzzle.

STEP 10

The barreled action is now free of the stock.

STEP 11

The barrel shroud is unscrewed from the receiver. This usually comes off easily with hand pressure only. If the shroud

did not unscrew easily, we would have thought seriously about how much we needed to remove it. They are fragile and could easily be damaged if more aggressive techniques are used. The more aggressive techniques generally involve the application of heat, and it is possible to discolor the metal with such an attempt.

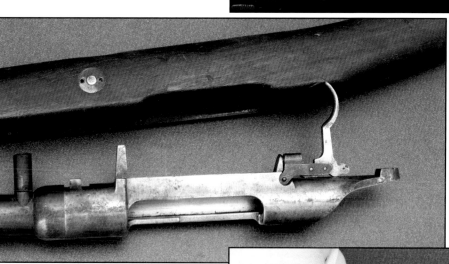

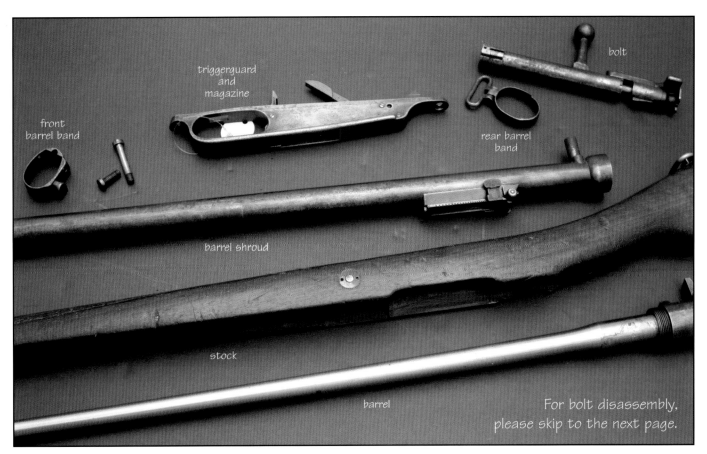

bolt

triggerguard
and
magazine

front
barrel band

rear barrel
band

barrel shroud

stock

barrel

For bolt disassembly,
please skip to the next page.

The Hanyang Commission Rifle

29-2

Aside from its obvious lack
of a barrel jacket, the
Hanyang differs from the
M1888 German "Com-
mission" rifle in that it
has a handguard, which
is removed as shown.
Note that it is easy to
damage this piece of wood, because the sight is under spring tension.

The front magazine
screw on the Hanyang
is a little shorter than on the German rifle
because there is no barrel jacket.

The Gew. 88 Bolt

Disassembly:

With the bolt in the left hand, the safety lever is pushed in with the thumb, and the striker nut on the end of the firing pin unscrewed.

The mainspring is slid over the firing pin.

The nut, the safety with its spring, and the cocking piece will now come off.

Holding the bolt housing in the left hand, the firing pin assembly is slid in with the bolt head's lug centered between the two lugs on the bolt housing.

Holding the bolt in the left hand, the bolt head is turned a quarter of a turn (i.e., 90°) in the direction away from the bolt handle.

The bolt head is then turned a quarter turn (i.e., 90°) towards the lug on the bolt housing that has a groove in it.

The bolt head is pulled straight out. The firing pin and main spring follow it.

The cocking piece slides onto the back of the firing pin with the safety housing directly in line with the base of the bolt.

The bolt is now disassembled to its basic component parts.

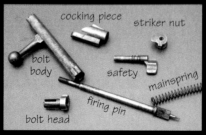

cocking piece · striker nut · bolt body · safety · mainspring · firing pin · bolt head

The safety is pushed into the housing.

Reassembly:

The firing pin slides into the bolt head with the flat spot on the firing pin aligned with the protruding lug on the bolt head.

flat spot

The safety is pressed in with a thumb while the striker nut is screwed down until the back of the mainspring is flush with the top of the nut. This last action compresses the spring, and requires some pressure and strength.

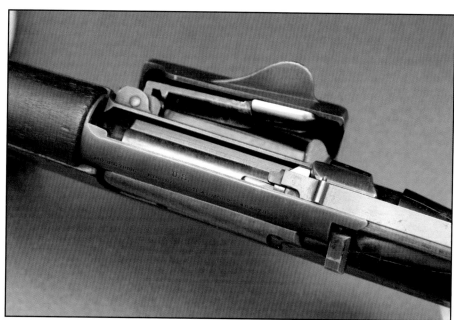

STEP 1

First, it is ensured that the rifle is not loaded and the magazine is empty. Note that this is a U.S. Model 1898 Rifle.

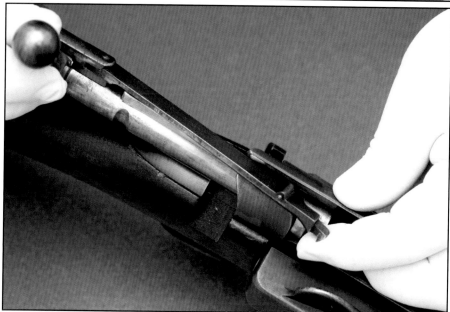

STEP 2

The bolt is removed by opening it and drawing it back as far as it will go. Then, the extractor is pulled up. As the bolt handle is turned towards the magazine, the extractor slips over on its pivot as shown. The bolt can now be pulled out of the rifle.

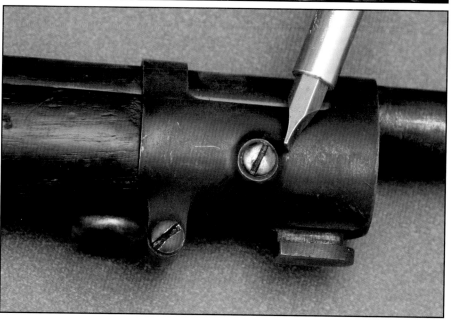

STEP 3

The front barrel band screw and the stacking swivel screw are both removed.

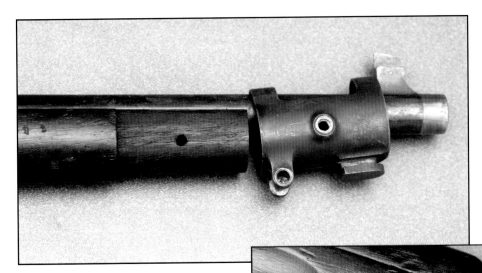

STEP 4

The barrel band is slid forward. It does not clear the front sight, so it is left in the position shown.

STEP 5

The rear barrel band screw is removed and the barrel band slipped as far forward as it will go.

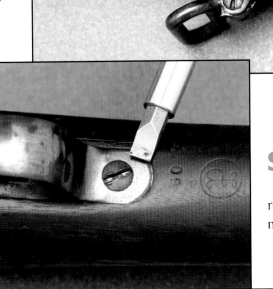

STEP 6

The screws at the front and rear of the triggerguard are removed.

STEP 7

The triggerguard is lifted out.

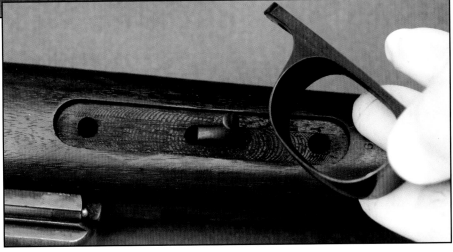

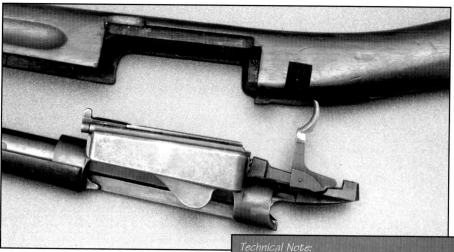

STEP 8

The barreled action comes away from the stock. Note that the handguard remains attached.

STEP 9

The handguard is removed by lifting its wider rear section and pushing it forward to clear the sight lock at the front. The handguard is fragile and easily broken. Taking it off risks damage.

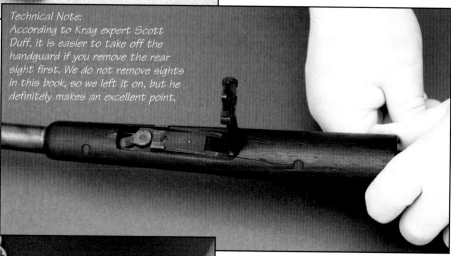

Technical Note:
According to Krag expert Scott Duff, it is easier to take off the handguard if you remove the rear sight first. We do not remove sights in this book, so we left it on, but he definitely makes an excellent point.

STEP 10

To relieve tension on the magazine spring, two pieces of soft wood and a C-clamp are gently employed as shown.

STEP 11

Now that the spring tension is relieved, the magazine gate hinge pin can be removed. The head of the pin is turned upward, as shown, so that it may be drawn out.

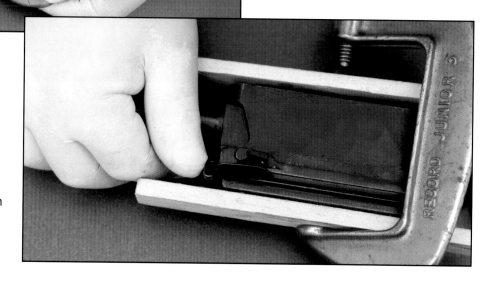

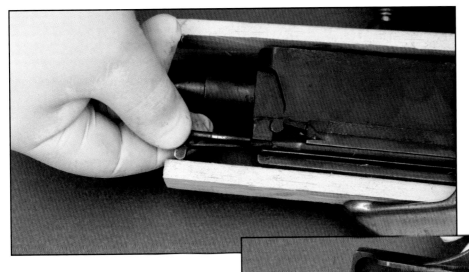

STEP 12

The pin is often tight and requires careful handling as it is easily bent. It should, however, be removable with hand strength only.

STEP 13

With its hinge pin removed, the magazine cover is lifted away from the action.

STEP 14

The magazine spring is lifted out of its slot.

STEP 15

The carrier and follower assembly is lifted so that its end clears the receiver, at which point it can be lifted out.

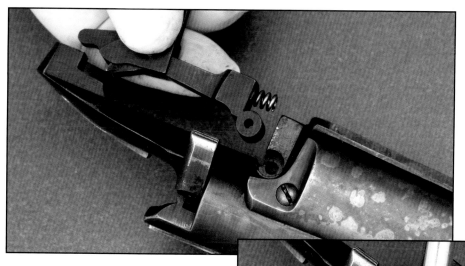

STEP 16

The trigger assembly is removed by pushing the trigger forward to clear the rear of the action and lifting it away from the action. Note that the spring seen at the left will come with it. The trigger itself is retained by a small pin that should only be disturbed if necessary.

STEP 17

A single screw holds the receiver sideplate in place.

STEP 18

With the screw out, the rear of the sideplate is lifted and the entire plate pulled off to the rear.

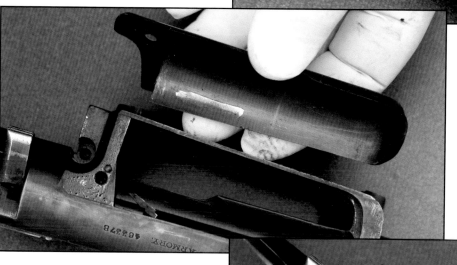

STEP 19

Under the plate, there is a threaded hole next to the head of a tiny pin. Lifting out this pin will free the ejector.

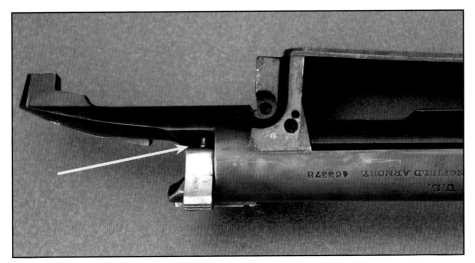

STEP 20

The magazine cut-off can be removed by compressing the tiny spring-loaded detent (see arrow) and pulling it out. As this can be very tricky to re-install, it probably should not be touched unless necessary.

Reassembly Notes

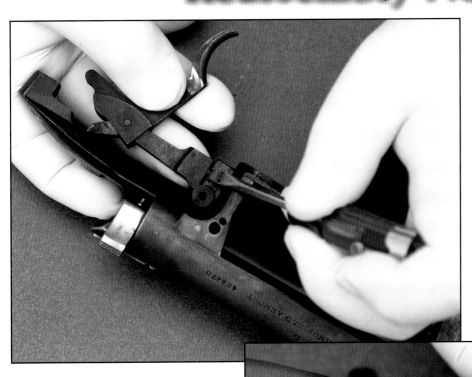

STEP 21

Reassembly of the Krag is basically a reversal of the disassembly, so most of it will not be covered here. However, the action is tricky enough to warrant some extra attention. First, the trigger is returned to its slot. Note that it was necessary to compress the trigger spring with the end of a small screwdriver.

STEP 22

The ejector is inserted in its slot (bottom of photo). While this is being done, the tiny pin that holds the ejector is returned to its hole (top of photo), securing it in place.

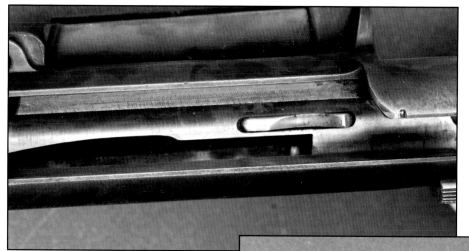

STEP 23

This is what the ejector should look like when it is returned to its proper place.

STEP 24

The sideplate is put back in place with its retaining screw.

STEP 25

The pin on the end of the carrier and follower is slipped into its hole, and the carrier and follower (a two-piece assembly) is dropped into the magazine.

STEP 26

The magazine spring is returned to its slot as shown. The curve goes up.

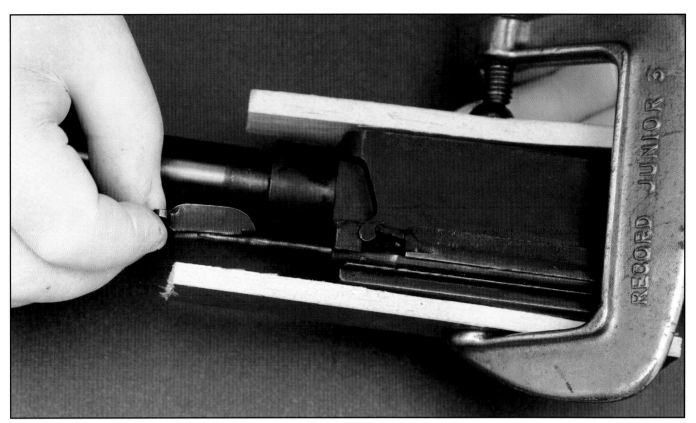

STEP 27

Using the two pieces of wood and the C-clamp from the disassembly steps, the magazine is gently compressed so that the holes for the magazine hinge pin line up with each other. Then, the magazine hinge pin is slid into place. This may require gentle tapping with a plastic hammer.

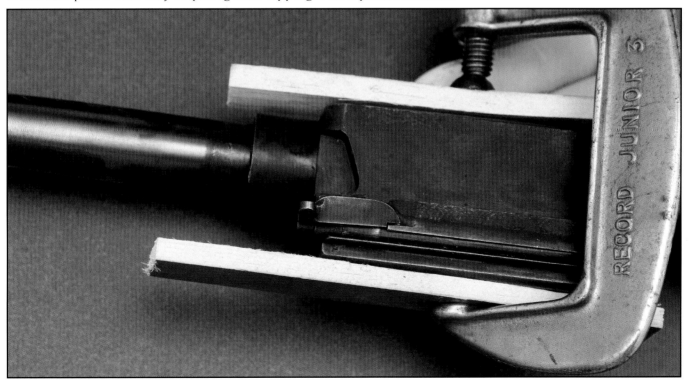

STEP 28

This is what the magazine hinge pin should look like when fully in place. Reassembly of the action is now complete.

M1898 Krag Bolt

Disassembly:

The cocking piece is pulled back and rotated in the direction of the bolt handle until the bolt snaps open.

This is what it looks like in the process of opening.

The mainspring is pulled back with one hand (see right side of photo) while the firing pin is pushed back a bit and then slid off the striker.

This shows the striker with the mainspring and firing pin removed as accomplished in the previous step.

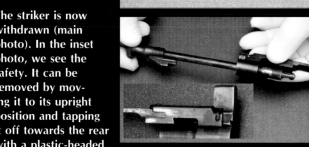

The striker is now withdrawn (main photo). In the inset photo, we see the safety. It can be removed by moving it to its upright position and tapping it off towards the rear with a plastic-headed hammer.

Reassembly:

The striker is slid back into place.

The spring is slid over the striker.

The spring is compressed with one hand while the firing pin is returned to its place. It slips over the end of the striker as shown, and then the firing pin is made straight so its little lugs catch in the notches in the striker.

This is what the firing pin assembly looks like put together.

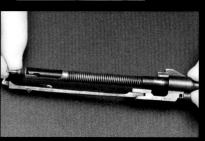

The firing pin assembly is slipped into the bolt body as shown here. Note the position of the safety.

Holding the bolt body and extractor with one hand, the cocking piece is pulled back and the firing pin assembly is pushed forward and twisted so that the lug on the bolt body fits under the extractor as shown.

The cocking piece is then pulled back a second time and rotated to the cocked position as shown in the picture. The bolt is now assembled.

The Early Mannlichers, Models 1886 through 1890

A Model 1886 Mannlicher shown above the Model 1888. The Model 1886 was used in the Chilean Civil War and this inset shows its stock cartouche.

STEP 1

For this disassembly, we chose the Model 1886 because it was in the worst condition of the rifles we own. For disassembly purposes, there is little difference between the models. For instance, the screw enters the nosecap from the opposite side on the Model 1888.

First, with the rifle pointed in a safe direction, it is ensured that it is unloaded and the magazine is empty.

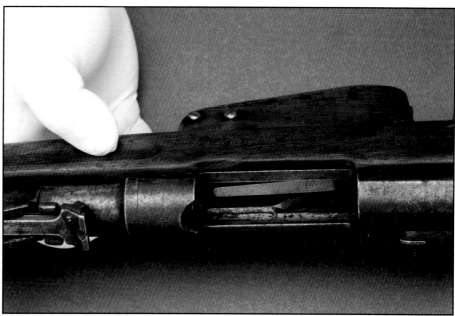

STEP 2

The screw retaining the nose-cap is taken out and the cap slid forward and off of the rifle.

STEP 3

The middle barrel band has its screw removed and is slid forward and off.

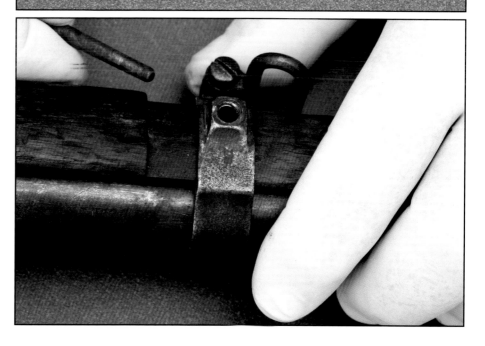

STEP 4

The rear barrel band is a little different, having a captured screw that is loosened (not taken out). The band can then be slid forward and off of the rifle.

STEP 5

The screw at the front of the magazine is taken out.

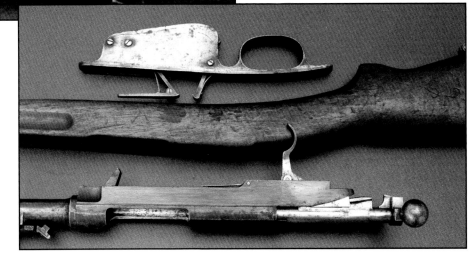

STEP 6

The screw at the rear of the magazine is taken out.

STEP 7

The barreled action and the magazine can now be pulled out of the stock.

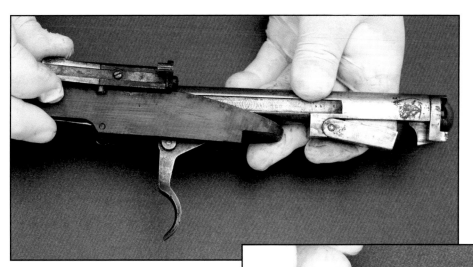

STEP 8

The bolt is removed by holding out the bolt stop and pulling the bolt straight back.

STEP 9

If necessary, the trigger and trigger spring can be removed by drifting out the pin indicated.

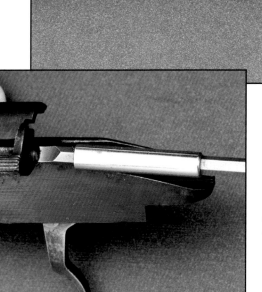

STEP 10

The screw at the rear of the action, which holds the safety in place, is removed.

STEP 11

The safety can now be taken out.

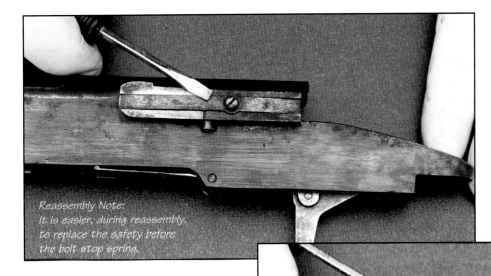

*Reassembly Note:
It is easier, during reassembly,
to replace the safety before
the bolt stop spring.*

STEP 12

The small screw retaining the bolt stop spring is removed and the spring lifted out of its slot.

STEP 13

The screw underneath the bolt stop is taken out.

STEP 14

The bolt stop can now be removed.

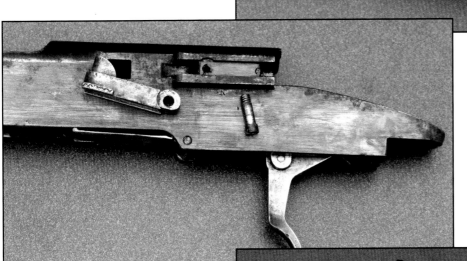

STEP 15

The magazine can be further dismantled by removing the three screws in its body. The inner parts can now be pulled out from the bottom of the action. However, these parts can be difficult to fit back into place, so this is not normally done unless necessary.

M86 Mannlicher Bolt

Disassembly:

The 1886 Manlicher bolt has little in common with other designs. First, the extractor is removed by gently prying up its tail end. It should pop out of the bolt body.

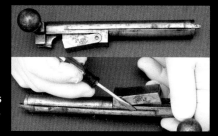

The bolt head is unscrewed from the bolt body.

The mainspring is compressed by inserting a piece of 5/16 automotive brake line with the flared end against the tip of the pin and pressing down on a block of wood. The cocking piece is then unscrewed.

With the cocking piece removed, the firing pin/striker and mainspring are released and the bolt handle slides out of the bolt body.

The firing pin/striker and mainspring. The locking lug (see arrow) can be removed by drifting out its pin, but this is seldom, if ever, necessary.

Reassembly:

The mainspring and firing pin/striker are inserted into the bolt body with the flat surface on the striker facing up as shown at the right.

The bolt handle is replaced, taking care that it engages the locking lug as shown at the right. There is a flat on the inside of this part that must align with the flat on the firing pin/striker.

The flared end of the 5/16 brake line is inserted in order to compress the mainspring.

Pressing down on a block of wood, the cocking piece is screwed onto the threaded end of the firing pin/striker.

When returned to its proper place, the cocking piece should be flush with the end of the firing pin/striker and slide into the slot in the bottom side of the bolt handle.

The bolt face is now screwed into the bolt body so that their extractor slots are aligned.

The extractor is now gently snapped into place and the bolt is reassembled. Note that in order to return the bolt to the rifle, the locking lug must be held as shown in the inset photo.

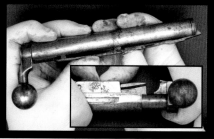

Mannlicher M95
Rifle and Carbine

STEP 1

For this disassembly, we have chosen a Model 1895 carbine because they are readily available on the surplus market. The Model 1895 rifle is almost identical and will be covered separately at the end of this section. First, with the muzzle pointed in a safe direction, we check that the rifle is unloaded, the magazine is empty and the bore is free of obstructions.

STEP 2

The bolt is removed by pulling the trigger forward while pulling the bolt backwards, out of the action. This is a straight pull rifle, so no rotation of the bolt handle is necessary.

STEP 3

The retaining screw/pin that passes through the front barrel band is removed.

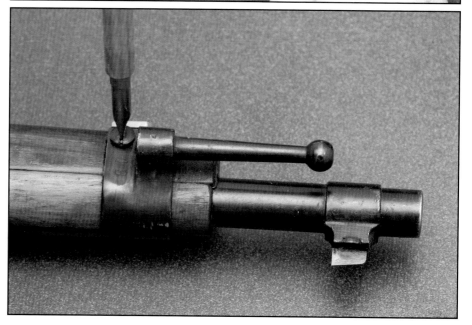

STEP 4

The front barrel band is slid off, over the front sight.

STEP 5

(left view) The screw/pin in the rear barrel band (that passes through the stock) is removed.

(middle view) The captured screw that tightens the rear barrel band is loosened. This screw does not come all the way out.

(right view) The rear barrel band is carefully slid forward off the stock.

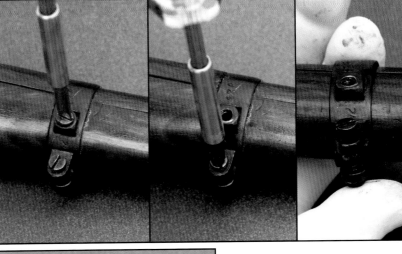

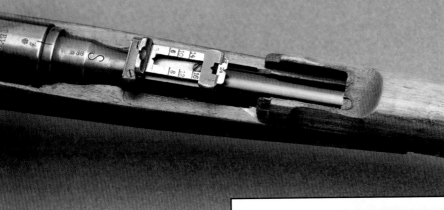

STEP 6

The handguard can now be lifted off.

STEP 7

The screw at the front of the magazine is taken out.

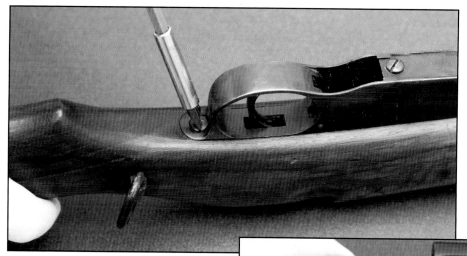

STEP 8

The screw at the rear of the triggerguard is taken out.

STEP 9

The magazine/triggerguard assembly is gently pulled down and out of the rifle.

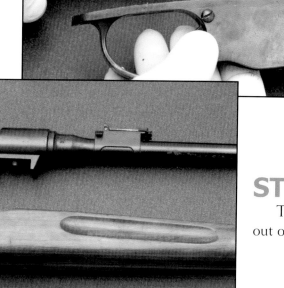

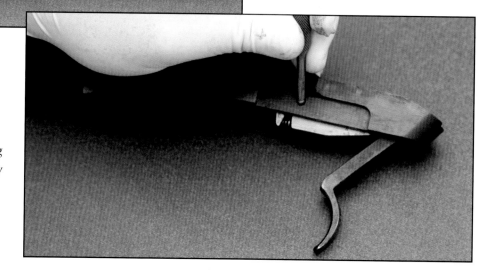

STEP 10

The barreled action is lifted out of the stock.

STEP 11

The trigger mechanism is freed by drifting out the retaining pin. This pin is generally not very tight.

STEP 12
The trigger mechanism can now be removed.

STEP 13
The rifle is now disassembled to its basic components. The magazine can be disassembled further, if needed, by removing all of its screws.

The Model 1895 Rifle

For disassembly purposes, our Model 1895 Mannlicher rifle is almost indistinguishable from our Model 1895 Mannlicher carbine. The sights are different and the screws on the barrel bands are aligned a bit different...but that's about it.

Mannlicher M95 Bolt

Disassembly:

The bolt should come out with its head extended. (If it doesn't, skip this step.) The bold head is tapped with a plastic hammer snapping it back in.

Holding the safety out of the way, the cocking piece is unscrewed and removed. It is under tension, so it is necessary to keep pulling back during this process.

With the cocking piece removed, a plastic hammer is used to tap on the threaded end of the firing pin. This drives all the pieces out.

These are the pieces that are now seen.

The nut on the end of the firing pin guide is unscrewed. The firing pin spring is compressed by this nut. This must be done carefully so the pin won't fly out.

The bolt is now disassembled to its component parts.

mainspring guide

firing pin/striker and mainspring

bolt body

extractor

nut

cocking piece

Reassembly:

The disassembly steps are reversed. Here we see how the firing pin and mainspring guide must be aligned. (See arrows for critical areas.)

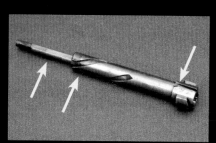

The firing pin assembly is slipped into the bolt body aligned as shown here with the flat portion of the firing pin facing towards the bolt handle. It should turn counterclockwise as it enters.

The bolt head is placed slightly away from the bolt body as shown in photo.

The extractor is tapped into its slot as shown, using a plastic hammer. This will drive the bolt head down flush with the bolt.

The cocking piece is screwed onto the rear of the firing pin.

Next, the bolt head is pulled out until it clicks. The bolt can be returned to the rifle. On some bolts, the head will not stay open. A coin can be used to hold it open (as shown). The bolt is slid into the action until the lugs are covered, the coin removed and the rest of the bolt inserted.

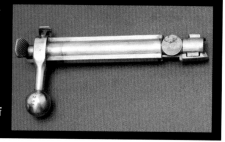

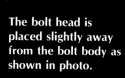

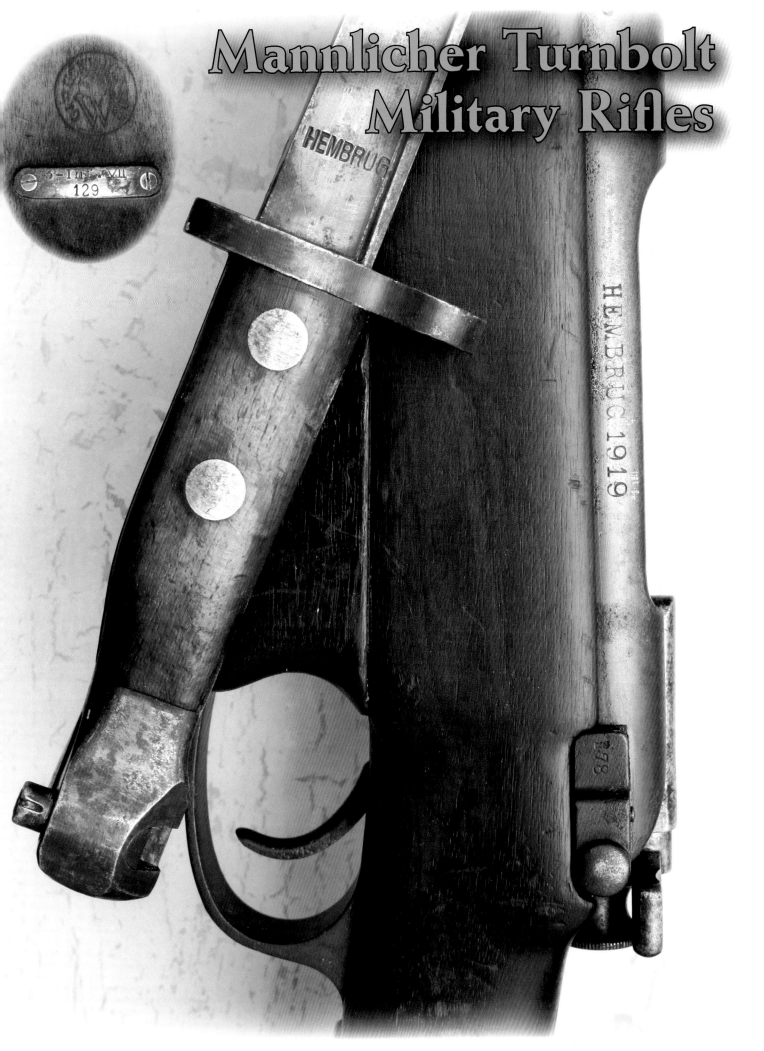

STEP 1

First, with the rifle pointed in a safe direction, it is ensured that it is unloaded and that its magazine is empty.

The bolt is then removed by depressing the spring-loaded bolt catch on the left side of the receiver and pulling the bolt out of the receiver.

This Dutch Mannlicher, a M1895 No. 1 Cavalry Carbine, appears here courtesy of Evans Kavallines.

STEP 2

The nosecap is removed by taking out its retaining screw and slipping it forward over the front sight.

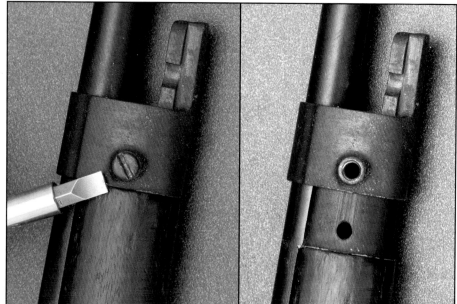

STEP 3

The screws at the front of the magazine and the rear of the trigger guard are removed.

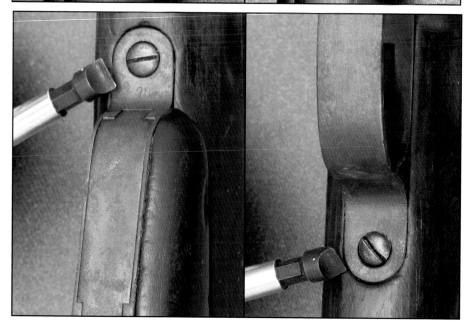

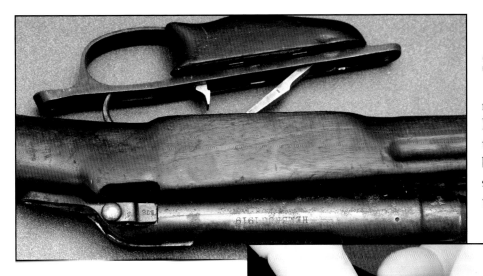

STEP 4

The barreled action and the magazine/triggerguard are now lifted out of the stock. Normally, the two sling swivels would now be removed from the stock (two screws each), but unfortunately, this carbine is missing them.

STEP 5

The wooden guard on the side of the magazine, unique to the Dutch Mannlichers, is removed by pressing it towards the top of the magazine.

STEP 6

With the wooden guard removed, the rifle's serial number can be seen stamped on its inner surface.

STEP 7

The spring-loaded bolt catch is removed by pressing out its retaining pin with the tip of a punch, pushing down from the top. It is not a friction fit and should come out with minimal pressure.

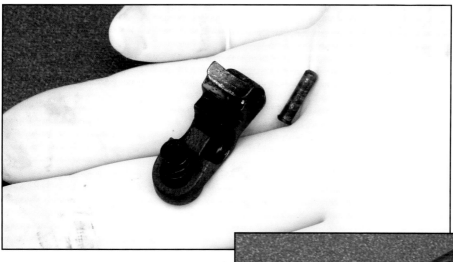

STEP 8

The bolt catch, its spring and retaining pin.

STEP 9

The trigger mechanism is removed by pressing out its retaining pin. Like the bolt catch pin, it is not a friction fit and should come out easily.

STEP 10

The trigger mechanism. Unless absolutely necessary, it isn't normally dismantled.

STEP 11

The magazine can be disassembled by removing the two screws that pass through it from side-to-side. With the screw removed, the cartridge follower (left side of photo) presses out to the front. The charger release lever (right side of photo) lifts out from the top.

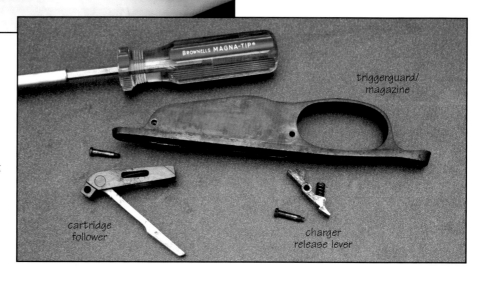

triggerguard/ magazine

cartridge follower

charger release lever

The Model 1903 Greek Mannlicher-Schoenauer

Before we move on to the Mannlicher Turnbolt's bolt, let's examine one of the more interesting varients of this type of rifle. The Greek Model 1903 Mannlicher-Schoenauer features a beautifully made rotary magazine. The steps for its removal are illustrated here. (John Wall collection)

Dutch M95 Bolt

Disassembly:

The bolt should come out of the rifle in the cocked position as shown here.

The cocking piece is rotated so that it fits against the bolt body as seen at the right. This releases pressure on the mainspring.

After the cocking piece has been turned, the bolt head is pulled out. As it is retained by a spring, it can be necessary to gently pry it forward with a small screwdriver.

With the tip of the firing pin pressed against a wooden block and the thumb depressing the safety, the nut on the end of the firing pin/striker is unscrewed.

This will release all of the bolt pieces. The spring exerts considerable pressure so it is important to be very careful releasing tension on the striker when the nut has been removed.

Reassembly:

The mainspring is slipped onto the firing pin/striker. The assembled unit is slipped into the bolt body.

Using a block of wood to protect the tip, the mainspring is compressed, forcing the end of the firing pin/striker out of the end of the bolt body. Note the position of the flat (see arrow).

The cocking piece is slipped on, and the safety and its spring returned to its slot. This is sometimes awkward.

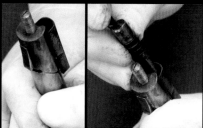

Holding the cocking piece and safety compressed with a thumb, the nut is screwed onto the end of the firing pin/striker.

When returned to its proper position, the file mark on the end of the nut will align with the slot-like mark on the end of the striker.

The bolt head is now pushed back into place. The tiny lug (see arrow) aligns with a slot inside the bolt. The bolt head should snap into place.

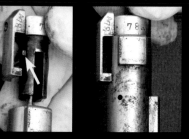

The cocking piece is then pulled back and rotated so that the bolt is in the cocked position. It is then returned to the rifle.

Italian
Carcano

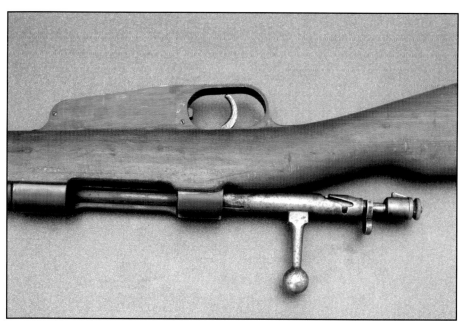

STEP 1

First, with the rifle pointed in a safe direction, it is ensured that it is unloaded and that its magazine is empty.

This Model 1891 Carcano appears here courtesy of Evans Kavallines.

STEP 2

The bolt is removed by opening and then withdrawing it while holding down the trigger.

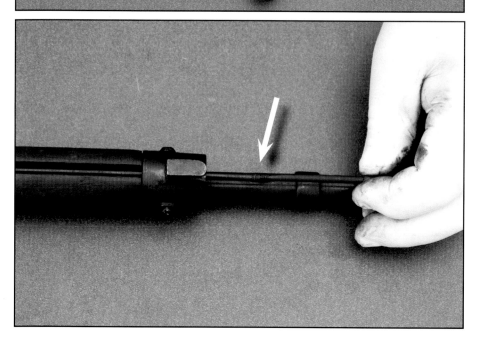

STEP 3

The cleaning rod is unscrewed from the nosecap (notice the unusually positioned threads) and withdrawn.

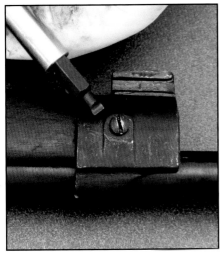

STEP 4

The nosecap screw is removed and the nosecap slipped off of the rifle over the front sight.

STEP 5

The barrel band retaining spring is depressed and the band slipped forward and off the rifle. Note that the handguard comes off during this process.

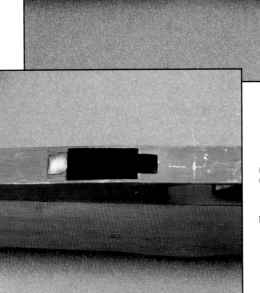

STEP 6

The screw at the front of the magazine is removed.

STEP 7

The screw at the rear of the triggerguard is removed.

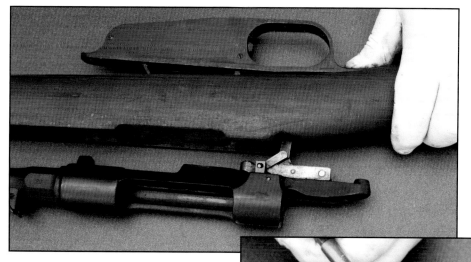

STEP 8

The barreled action and magazine are now lifted from the stock.

STEP 9

The rear sling swivel can be removed by taking out the two screws shown.

STEP 10

The buttplate is removed by taking out its two retaining screws.

STEP 11

The trigger mechanism is held together by pins. In theory, this can be taken apart, but gunsmiths recommend against doing this unless absolutely necessary.

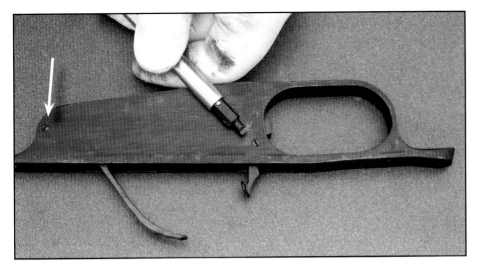

STEP 12

The charger release and its spring can be removed by taking out the screw indicated. The spring-loaded cartridge follower is held in place with another screw (see arrow), which can also be removed if necessary.

The Model 1938 Short Rifle

M1938 Short Rifle in 7.35 caliber with its 4th pattern M1938 knife bayonet. This example was sent

to Finland by the Italians during WWII and features the well-known "SA" mark of the Finnish Army.

The only difference for disassembly are the screws shown here.

The Carcano Bolt

Disassembly:

The Carcano bolt as it comes out of the rifle. M1891 rifle bolts have a straight handle while carbine and later rifle bolts are bent down.

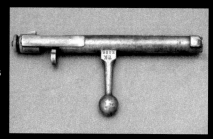

The cocking piece is rotated 1/4 turn counterclockwise to relieve pressure on the mainspring.

The nut on the end of the striker/firing pin is unscrewed. It is necessary to depress the tiny spring-loaded plunger (see arrow) in order to make the first two or three revolutions.

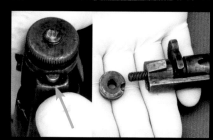

The cocking piece is now pulled off the rear of the bolt.

The safety is removed by pressing it in and rotating it counter-clockwise so that the tiny pin (see arrow) moves up the slot in the bolt body to the position shown in the right-hand photo.

The safety pops out, releasing the firing pin/striker and main-spring. The notch (see arrow) is absent on some bolts, but there is an internal groove in the same place.

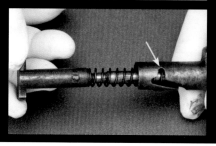

The striker/firing pin and mainspring removed from the bolt body. The bolt is now fully disassembled.

Reassembly:

The striker/firing pin and mainspring are returned to the bolt body with the flat (see arrow) oriented as shown in the top photo.

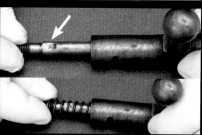

The safety is returned to the bolt, making sure that the pin (see arrows) enters the internal groove. The safety is pushed in and rotated so that the pin returns to its original position.

The cocking piece is now pushed onto the rear of the striker/fir-ing pin. Note that the flat portion of the pin is aligned with the bolt handle.

The nut is screwed onto the end of the striker/firing pin. It is necessary to depress the spring-loaded plunger in order for it to complete the last two or three turns.

The cocking piece is now pulled back and rotated 1/4 turn clockwise to return the bolt to the cocked position. It is now ready to be returned to the rifle.

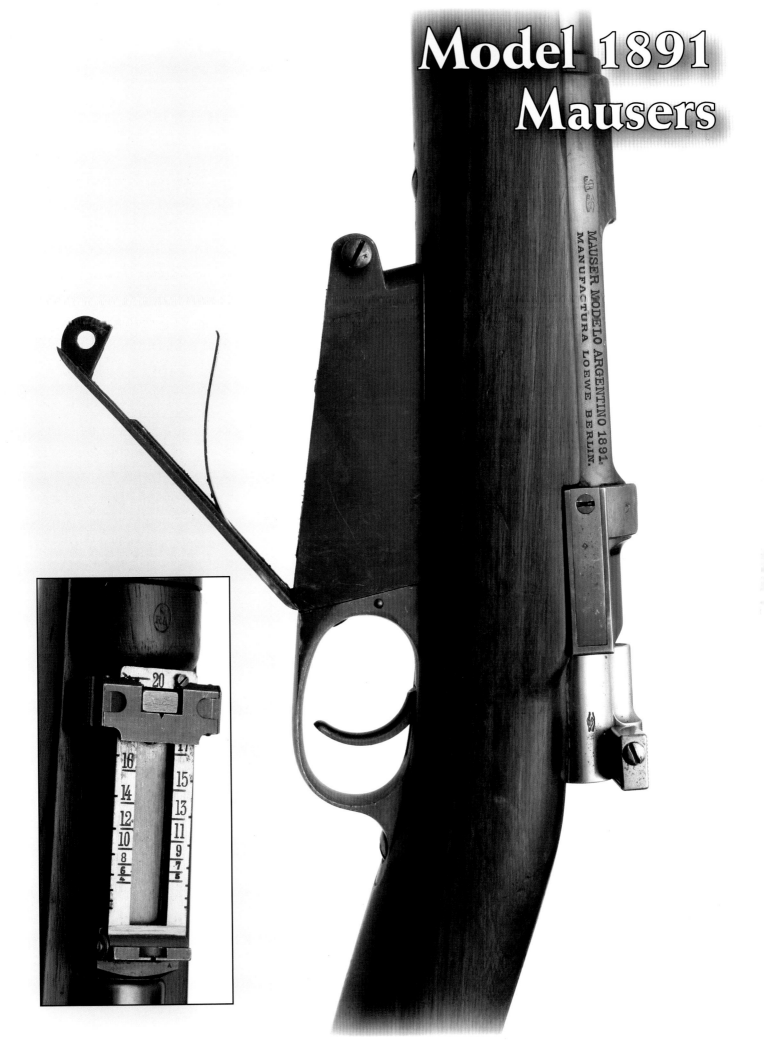

Model 1891
Mausers

STEP 1

Having confirmed that the rifle is unloaded, the bolt is removed in the same fashion as most Mausers, by opening it and pulling it straight back while holding the catch (see arrow) open.

Other than the magazine and bolt, these early smokeless powder Mausers are essentially similar to the later versions covered in the section on "Mauser Rifles and Carbines, Models 1892-96."

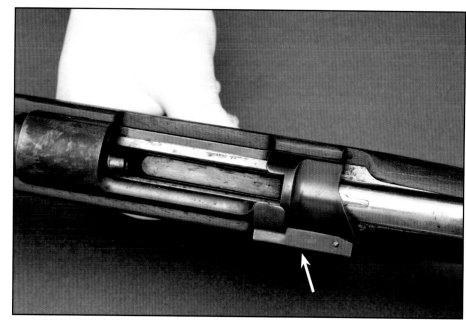

STEP 2

The front and rear screws are removed from the magazine/triggerguard assembly. Note that some variations of this rifle also have an additional, large locking screw in front of the magazine, which also needs to be removed.

STEP 3

The triggerguard (with the magazine attached) is pulled down and out of the rifle.

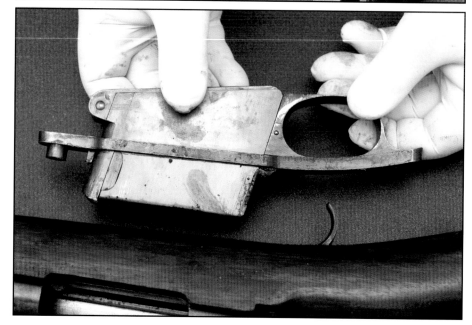

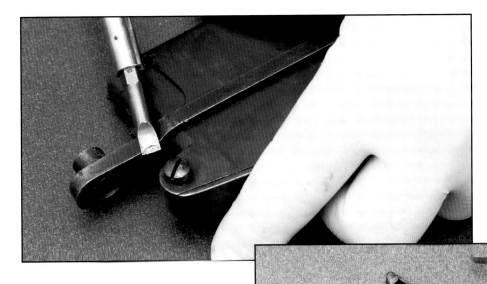

STEP 4

The screw at the front edge of the magazine is removed.

STEP 5

The lower part of the magazine is now opened, releasing the spring-loaded cartridge follower mechanism.

STEP 6

The magazine itself is removed from the triggerguard by pushing in the tiny button located inside the front of the triggerguard to release it, and pulling the magazine down and out of its slot.

STEP 7

The barreled action is now lifted out of the stock. In the case of this M1891 Argentine rifle, the handguard remains attached to the barrel and is only removed after the barrel is separated from the stock.

Mauser M1891 Bolt

Disassembly:

The bolt on this rifle comes out in the same fashion as the later Mauser bolts. Once out, a block of wood is used to hold the cocking piece open.

With the cocking piece open, a coin is inserted as shown.

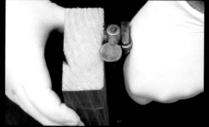

The bolt sleeve, with the attached firing pin and mainspring, is unscrewed from the bolt body.

The cocking piece is unscrewed from the firing pin while pressing the tip of the firing pin against a block of wood and pushing down on the bolt sleeve. Unlike many other Mausers, it is actually threaded on.

Smaller parts of the disassembled bolt. We have left the safety and extractor in place.

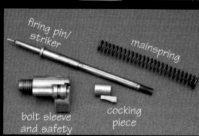

firing pin/striker

mainspring

bolt sleeve and safety

cocking piece

Reassembly:

The mainspring is slipped onto the firing pin.

The firing pin and mainspring are slipped into the bolt sleeve. Note that there is a little flat portion on the firing pin (see arrow) that aligns with a notch in the bolt sleeve.

With the tip of the mainspring pressed against a block of wood, the bolt sleeve is pushed down, compressing the mainspring. The cocking piece is then screwed on.

The assembled parts are then slid into the bolt body and screwed down.

As the cocking sleeve approaches the bolt body, it is necessary to push the cocking piece (see arrow) back during the last two or three turns. The cocking sleeve touches the bolt handle when fully seated.

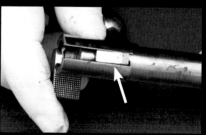

We did not remove the extractor. These M1891 extractors proved to be fragile in service; note how small it is in this photo. Later Mauser designs include a much more substantial version. In theory, M1891 extractors are removed by pushing up on the extractor hook with a screwdriver and prying the extractor forward over the bolt face.

STEP 1

To represent these rifles, we chose a Swedish M41B Sniper Rifle. Since we shoot this rifle, we chose not to mess with the scope mount and trigger. Samco Global of Miami, Florida kindly supplied the example shown here (www. samcoglobal.com). As always, it is first ensured that the rifle and its magazine are unloaded.

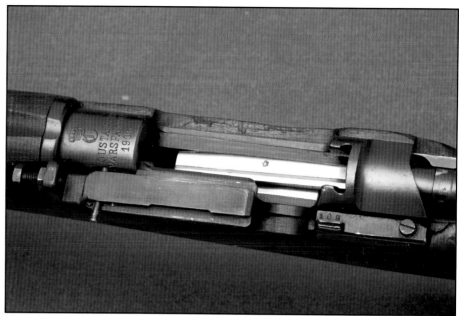

STEP 2

The bolt is removed by rotating the handle up and pulling it to the rear while holding open the bolt stop.

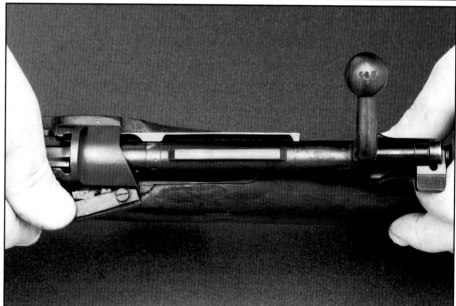

STEP 3

The cleaning rod is unscrewed and pulled out.

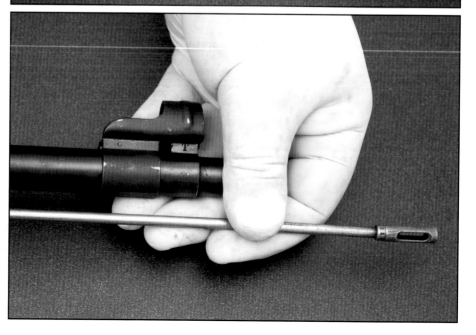

STEP 4

The nosecap is removed by holding down its spring with a bit of soft wood and then tapping forward as shown.

STEP 5

The barrel band is loosened and pushed forward in the same fashion. Note that on this rifle there is a large front sight assembly and the bands do not come all the way off the rifle.

STEP 6

The floorplate is removed by pushing in its spring catch with the body of a plastic pen, and then pushing the floorplate toward the triggerguard.

STEP 7

The screws at the front and rear of the triggerguard, which also hold the action in place, are taken out.

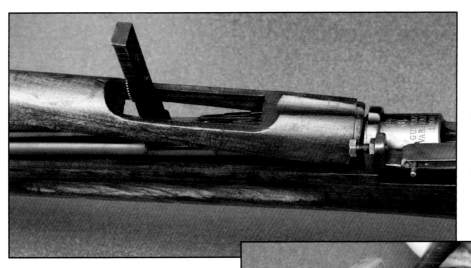

STEP 8

The handguard is gently lifted up and pulled towards the muzzle. Note that it is easy to damage this piece of wood, either where it meets the breech or around the rear sight.

STEP 9

The barreled actions on these rifles are often tight. One gentle way to remove them is to replace the screw shown and tap its head until the action comes loose.

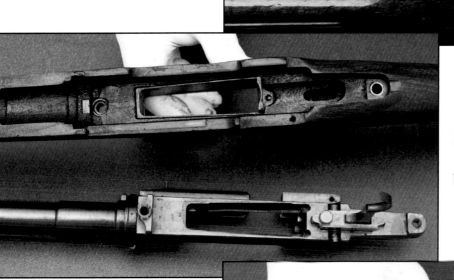

STEP 10

The barreled action can now be lifted from the stock.

STEP 11

The magazine can also be very tight. A small drift made from wood can be used to dislodge it while making an effort not to chip the surrounding wood.

STEP 12

The rear sling swivel and buttplate can be removed by taking out two screws for each.

STEP 13

The bolt stop screw is withdrawn. Note that this has a very sharp tip.

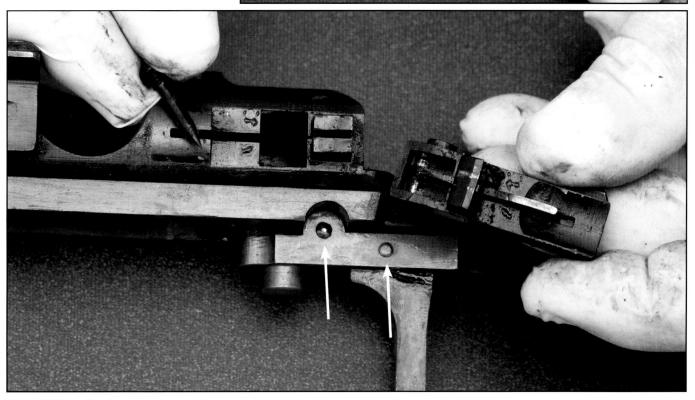

STEP 14

With its retaining screw removed, the bolt stop comes loose. Since this rifle has excellent trigger pull, we chose not to disassemble it. However, this is a simple matter of drifting out the two pins indicated.

Mauser 1896 Bolt

Disassembly:

The Model 1896 Mauser bolt in its assembled form. This bolt is very similar to other Mausers of the 1892–96 Model years.

The cocking piece is pulled back and held in place by moving the safety to its "straight up" position.

The bolt sleeve, with its attached parts, is unscrewed from the bolt body. It should come out very easily.

The extractor is removed from the bolt body by rotating it until the head is out of its groove in the bolt body. The extractor is then pushed forward and off.

With the tip of the firing pin against a block of wood, the bolt sleeve is pushed down until the cocking piece can be rotated one-quarter turn (in either direction) and lifted off.

The safety is removed by turning it as shown and pulling it out.

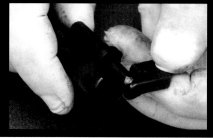

Reassembly:

The bolt is now disassembled and reassembly begins. First the extractor is replaced by sliding it back onto the bolt body and rotating it until it engages its groove and covers the solid locking lug.

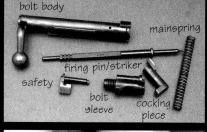

bolt body

mainspring

firing pin/striker

safety

bolt sleeve

cocking piece

The safety is returned to the bolt sleeve and turned as shown.

The mainspring is slipped over the firing pin and the two parts inserted into the bolt sleeve.

Using a block of wood to protect the tip of the firing pin, the bolt sleeve is pushed down until the cocking piece can be turned onto the firing pin (1/4 turn in either direction). The projection on the cocking piece goes into the slot in the bolt sleeve.

The cocking piece is pulled out and held in place by moving the safety to the "straight up" position.

The assembled parts are now screwed into the bolt body until the point where they stop. The bolt is now returned to the rifle.

The 1898 Mauser Rifles and 98k Carbines

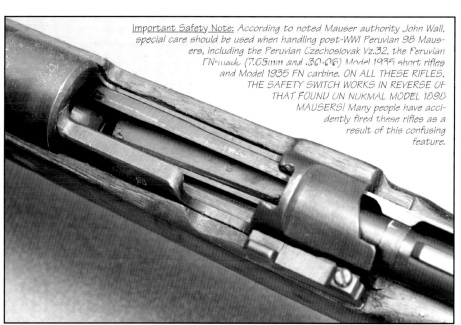

STEP 1

First, it is ensured that the rifle is not loaded. This K98k is one of the Russian refinished examples that are widely available today. Because of this rough, dark finish, these rifles can be more difficult to disassemble than original-condition German rifles.

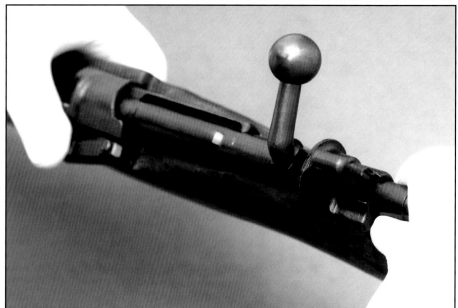

STEP 2

The bolt is opened and closed, leaving it in a cocked state. The safety is moved straight up as shown here. The bolt handle is then turned to its upmost position and the bolt drawn out of the rifle while holding open the bolt stop lever.

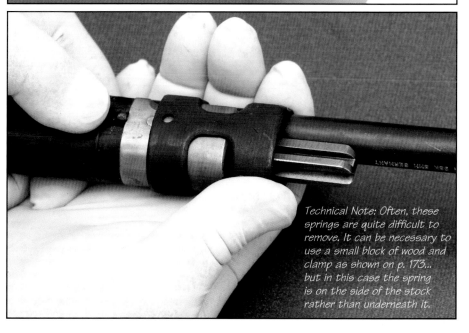

STEP 3

The cleaning rod is removed, and then the nose cap is slipped off by depressing its retaining spring. This piece can be stubborn and often requires loosening with a plastic-headed hammer, sometimes aided by a wood block.

Technical Note: Often, these springs are quite difficult to remove. It can be necessary to use a small block of wood and clamp as shown on p. 173... but in this case the spring is on the side of the stock rather than underneath it.

STEP 4

The spring is then lifted out.

STEP 5

The barrel band can then be slid off.

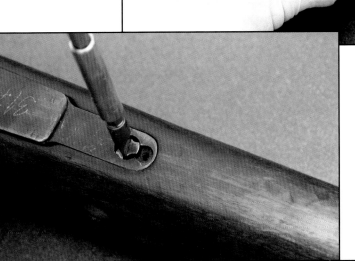

STEP 6

The screw at the front of the magazine is removed. On original-condition examples of this carbine, this screw is retained by a small set screw, which also has to be removed. The Russian refinishers often threw these out, so it is not present on this rifle.

STEP 7

The screw at the rear of the triggerguard is taken out.

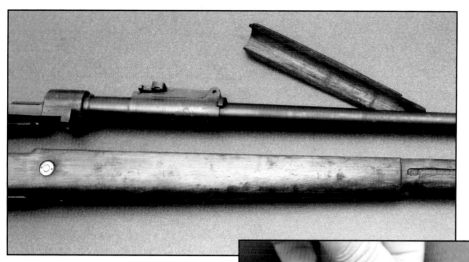

STEP 8

The barreled action and hand-guard are now loose and can be removed.

STEP 9

The magazine/triggerguard assembly is pulled out of the stock. These are often tight and care is needed not to damage the wood.

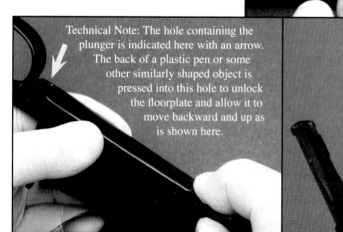

Technical Note: The hole containing the plunger is indicated here with an arrow. The back of a plastic pen or some other similarly shaped object is pressed into this hole to unlock the floorplate and allow it to move backward and up as is shown here.

STEP 10

(left view) The floorplate is removed by pressing in the recessed plunger at its back edge and pushing the floorplate toward the triggerguard.

(right view) The magazine spring can then be slipped out of its slot in the floorplate.

STEP 11

The bolt stop screw is removed.

The bolt stop is now loose and can be removed from the action (see inset, top right).

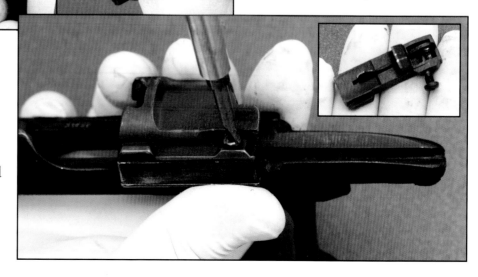

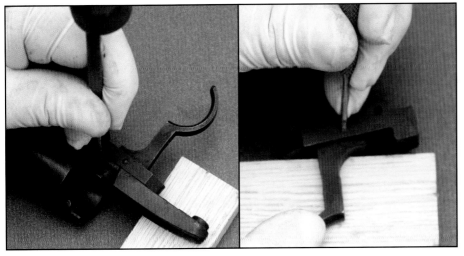

STEP 12

(left view) The sear pin is driven out with a punch. The sear/trigger assembly is removed. The sear spring is now loose and can be removed.

(right view) The trigger pin is now tapped out to finish the disassembly.

Other 1898-Style Mausers

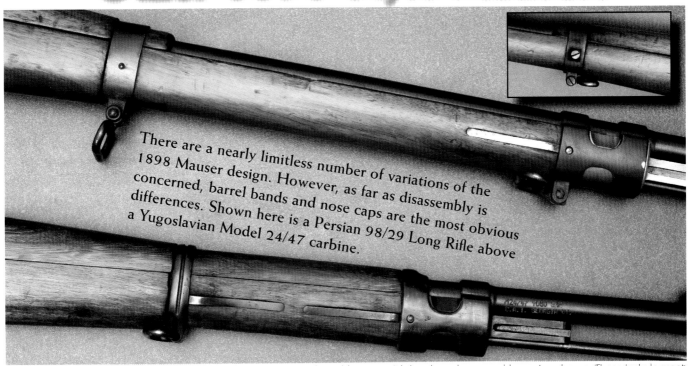

There are a nearly limitless number of variations of the 1898 Mauser design. However, as far as disassembly is concerned, barrel bands and nose caps are the most obvious differences. Shown here is a Persian 98/29 Long Rifle above a Yugoslavian Model 24/47 carbine.

The only variation that requires any real, special attention are those Mausers with handguards secured by spring clamps. These include most pre-WWI South American Model 1898 export Mausers, as well as all Vz. 24s and FN 98s. First, there is a large screw at the front of the rear sight that needs to be removed. The band is then slipped forward and off the handguard. There is a hidden clamp under the handguard

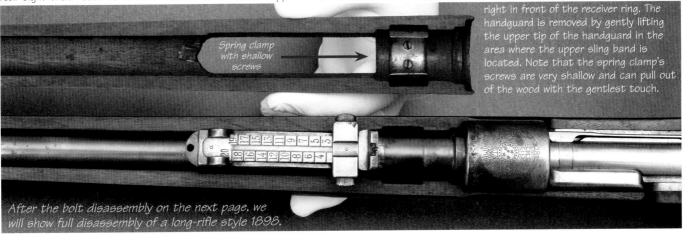

Spring clamp with shallow screws

right in front of the receiver ring. The handguard is removed by gently lifting the upper tip of the handguard in the area where the upper sling band is located. Note that the spring clamp's screws are very shallow and can pull out of the wood with the gentlest touch.

After the bolt disassembly on the next page, we will show full disassembly of a long-rifle style 1898.

K98k Mauser Bolt

Disassembly:

The little plunger (indicated by an arrow) is pushed in, and the whole assembly at right is screwed off counterclockwise.

This photo shows it coming apart.

The extractor is rotated out of its groove (towards the two holes in the bolt body) and is put in a position where the two holes are covered.

The extractor is pushed forward and off.

The tip of the firing pin is stuck into the purpose-built bushing in the side of the stock.

Pushing the bolt sleeve (bottom of photo below) down as far as it will go, the safety (see arrow) is moved to the "off" position, which is furthest to the left. The cocking piece (at top) is then rotated 1/4 turn and pulled off.

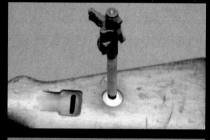

cocking piece

Once the cocking piece is off, the parts will come apart. They are under spring tension, so care is required to avoid injury.

The safety is rotated all the way to the right and pulled out (see left photo). The plunger is removed by pushing it and twisting it through the center slot (see right photo).

Reassembly Notes:

The spring slides on the firing pin and the bolt sleeve is slipped over its end and pressed down hard using the bushing in the stock as shown.

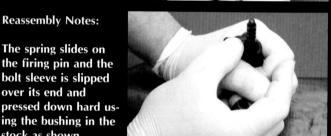

The cocking piece is slipped on and rotated 1/4 turn so that it lines up as shown (left photo). The safety is put in the straight up position (right photo).

The collar on the bolt body is located as shown and the extractor slid over it and into place. The extractor is now rotated until it falls back into the groove along the lip of the bolt head. The single lug behind the groove should be covered by the body of the extractor.

The assembled unit is screwed into the bolt body, pushing the retaining pin when necessary.

Turkish Model 1903/39 Mauser

Since Mauser 98s are so popular, let's do another variation!

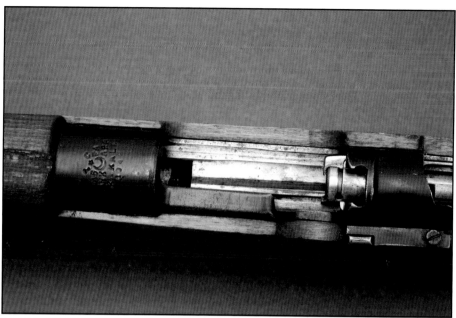

STEP 1

It is confirmed that the rifle and its magazine are unloaded.

STEP 2

The bolt release is opened and the bolt is removed, making sure that the safety is in a straight up-and-down position.

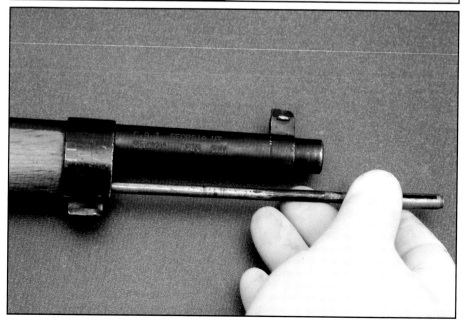

STEP 3

The cleaning rod is withdrawn. There is a captured nut inside the stock that it screws into, so it may be necessary to unscrew it first.

STEP 4

The front barrel band spring is compressed using a plastic clamp with a small piece of soft wood against the spring.

STEP 5

The barrel band is tapped off forward using a plastic hammer.

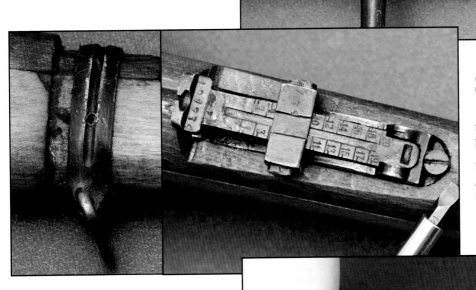

STEP 6

The screw at the front of the rear sight is removed as is the rear barrel band. This barrel band was retained with a nail, although others may have screws and/or barrel band springs.

STEP 7

With the sight screw and barrel band removed, the handguard can be lifted off and twisted so that its opening clears the adjustable slide on the sight.

STEP 8

The floorplate is removed by depressing the spring-loaded catch next to the triggerguard and pushing the plate towards the rear. This example was very tight and it was necessary to tap its forward edge with a wooden block and plastic hammer.

STEP 9

The set screw that secures the rear triggerguard screw is removed.

STEP 10

The rear triggerguard screw is now taken out.

STEP 11

The screw at the front of the triggerguard is removed. In this case, the retaining set screw was missing.

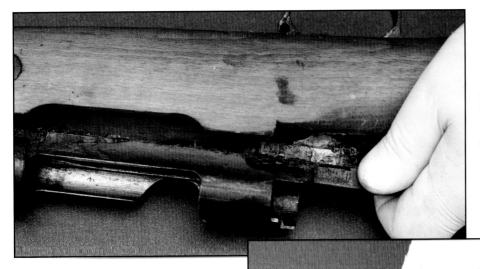

STEP 12

The barrelled action is pulled up and out of the stock.

STEP 13

The triggerguard/magazine can now be removed. Because this one was tight in the stock, a small drift was used to gently tap it down from the top.

STEP 14

The magazine/triggerguard can now be removed by pulling down and away from the stock.

STEP 15

The rear sling swivel and buttplate are removed by taking out their wood screws. Reassembly of this rifle is accomplished by reversing the above steps.

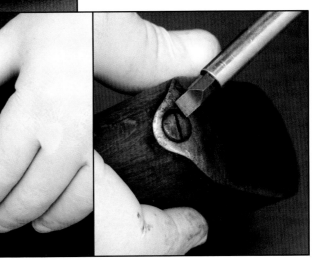

Turk M1903/39 Bolt

Disassembly:

The bolt is removed from the rifle with the safety in the "straight up" position. The bolt sleeve retaining pin is pushed in (see arrow).

The bolt sleeve is unscrewed, exposing the firing pin and the main spring. The bolt body is set aside.

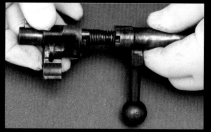

Using a block of wood to protect the tip of the firing pin, the mainspring is compressed by pushing down the bolt sleeve. The cocking sleeve (top of photo) is removed by turning it 1/4 turn in either direction.

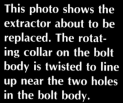

This releases all the major components as shown.

The safety is removed by turning it to the direction shown in the picture and pulling it out.

The extractor on the bolt body is rotated so that its head comes out of the groove that it rides in, as shown.

The extractor is now pushed forward (towards the left of the photo) to release it from the extractor collar. It should now come entirely off.

Reassembly Notes:

This photo shows the extractor about to be replaced. The rotating collar on the bolt body is twisted to line up near the two holes in the bolt body.

The extractor is replaced by sliding the groove on the underside of the extractor over the projection on the bolt body's collar.

The extractor is then rotated until its head (far right) snaps into the bolt body's groove. The extractor should cover the locking lug as shown (see arrow).

The firing pin, mainspring and bolt sleeve are put together (reversing disassembly). The mainspring is compressed (protecting firing pin tip with wood block), while the cocking sleeve is slipped on and turned to the position shown.

The assembled unit is screwed into the bolt body, pushing in the retaining pin when necessary. The safety is turned "straight up."

The Mukden Type 13 Mauser

Rifle and disassembly notes courtesy of John Wall. Note that like Arisakas, the varnish on these rifles is made from a plant similar to the Poison Oak, and can cause allergic reactions if inhaled while sanding the stocks.

Mukden Mauser Bolt

Disassembly:

The Mukden Mauser disassembles similarly to the M1898, except for the bolt, which will be illustrated here. With the bolt still in the rifle, the safety is set in the 12 o'clock position, the bolt release catch is pushed and the bolt is withdrawn.

With the bolt withdrawn, the firing pin assembly is rotated clockwise about 250 degrees.

The firing pin assembly is now withdrawn.

With the firing pin pointed in a safe direction, the bolt sleeve is held with one hand while the other hand rotates the safety 90 degrees to the left. The sleeve and firing pin are under pressure and will quickly come apart.

Unlike other Model 98s, the Mukden spring is inside the firing pin as shown and will easily slide out. This feature is shared by the Arisaka.

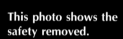

The safety is removed by rotating the collar (see arrow) from the position shown here until it is open on the top...see next step.

Once the collar has been rotated to this position, the safety can be turned all the way to the right (i.e., the safe position) and withdrawn.

This photo shows the safety removed.

Reassembly Note:

After the safety is re-installed and locked in place by rotating the collar, the bolt sleeve assembly is inserted into the firing pin with the safety in the firing position.

Note how the groove (white arrow) must be aligned with the safety pivot (yellow arrow).

Taking care not to move the collar off center, the assembly is pressed down until the front edge of the bolt sleeve is half over the first open hole as shown by the pointing finger.

Once it reaches the desired position (under a lot of pressure) the safety is rotated to the 12 o'clock position, which should lock it in place.

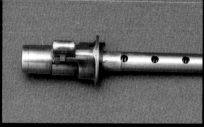

The firing pin assembly is inserted into the bolt body and rotated clockwise to the position shown. Note that the Mukden Mauser bolt sleeve does not lock into position.

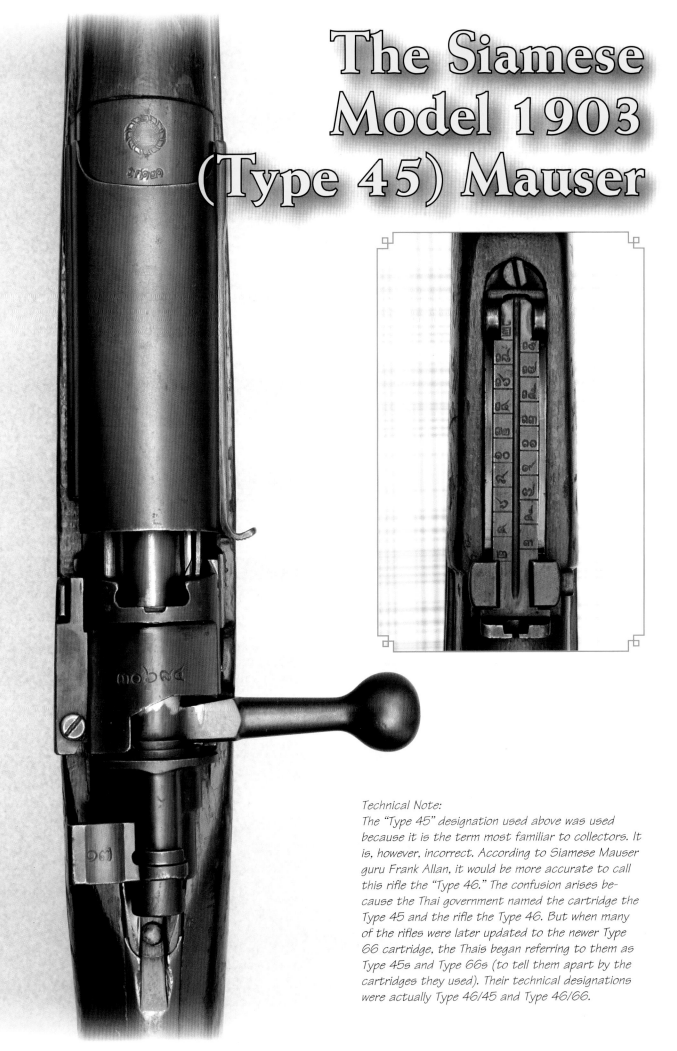

The Siamese Model 1903 (Type 45) Mauser

Technical Note:

The "Type 45" designation used above was used because it is the term most familiar to collectors. It is, however, incorrect. According to Siamese Mauser guru Frank Allan, it would be more accurate to call this rifle the "Type 46." The confusion arises because the Thai government named the cartridge the Type 45 and the rifle the Type 46. But when many of the rifles were later updated to the newer Type 66 cartridge, the Thais began referring to them as Type 45s and Type 66s (to tell them apart by the cartridges they used). Their technical designations were actually Type 46/45 and Type 46/66.

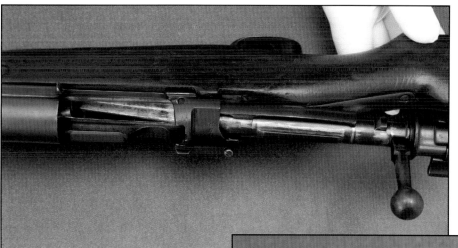

STEP 1

With the rifle pointed in a safe direction and the dustcover slid to the open position, it is ensured that the rifle is unloaded and its magazine empty. Note that this example is a Type 46/66.

STEP 2

Like all other Model 1898-style Mausers, the bolt is removed by moving the safety to its straight up position, opening the bolt, and withdrawing it while holding the bolt stop open.

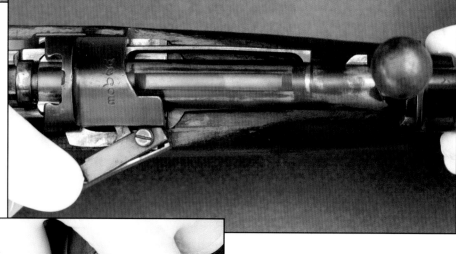

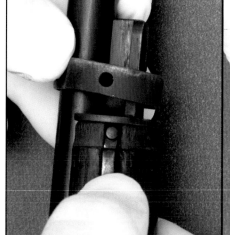

STEP 3

The barrel bands are removed by depressing their retaining springs and sliding the bands forward and off the rifle.

STEP 4

The dustcover is slid back and out of the way. The rear sight is opened to its extended position as shown. The handguard is then pulled gently forward and up, rotating it so that it passes over the sight and off the rifle.

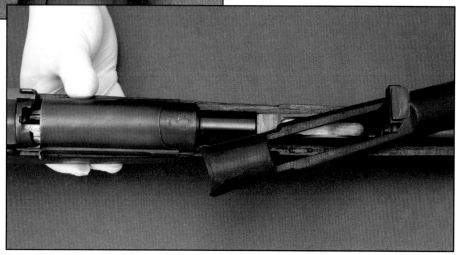

STEP 5

The screws at the front of the magazine and the rear of the triggerguard are removed.

STEP 6

The barreled action is pulled away from the stock.

STEP 7

The magazine floorplate is removed by pressing the knurled button inside the triggerguard while pushing the floorplate towards the triggerguard bow.

STEP 8

The magazine/triggerguard assembly is lifted from the stock.

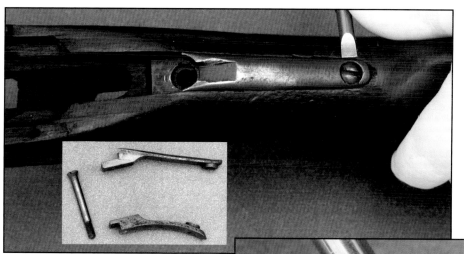

STEP 9

The reenforcing "tang" at the top of the wrist is removed by taking out its screw. There is a corresponding piece at the bottom, held in by the same screw, which also comes out in this step (see inset).

STEP 10

The rear sling swivel can be removed by taking out its two screws as shown.

STEP 11

The buttplate, with its sliding cover for the oiler, can be taken out by removing two screws.

STEP 12

The bolt stop can be removed by taking out the pointed screw shown. See this book's other M1898 Mauser disassemblies for a more detailed explanation of this step.

The bolt disassembles like other M1898 bolts shown in this book, so that information will not be repeated here.

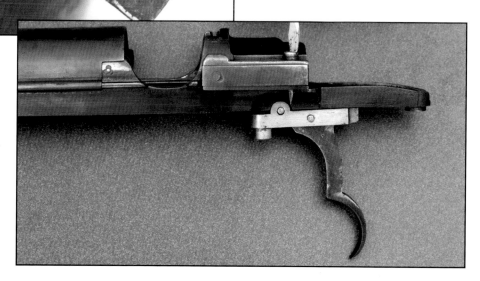

The U.S. Model 1903 Springfield

STEP 1

With the rifle pointed in a safe direction, it is ensured that it is unloaded and that its magazine is empty.

For this disassembly, we have chosen a Model 1903A1 Springfield that was refurbished for use in World War II. This rifle appears here courtesy of the Donald St.Germain collection.

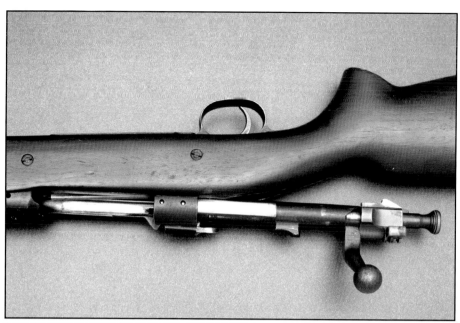

STEP 2

The bolt is closed and the safety is moved to the straight-up position (see arrow on the right) while the magazine cut-off is moved to its middle position (see arrow on the left). The bolt is now opened and pulled straight back and out of the receiver.

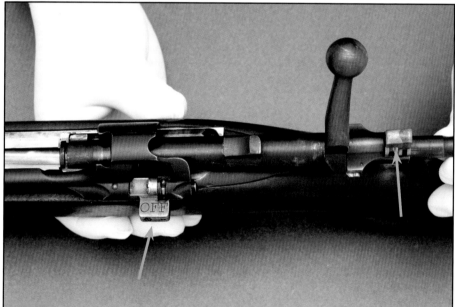

STEP 3

The front sling swivel screw is loosened and the screw passing through the nosecap is removed. The nosecap is then slid forward and off the stock. Because it will not pass over the front sight, it is left on the barrel.

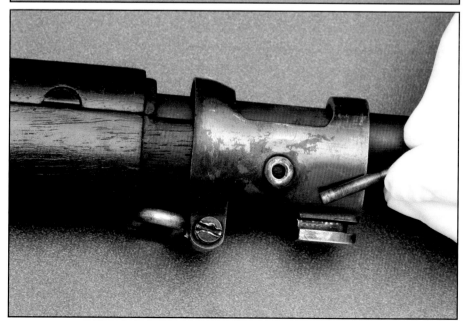

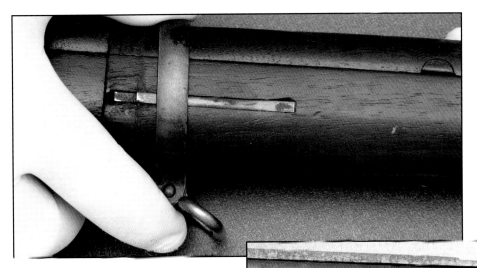

STEP 4

The screw holding the sling swivel to the barrel band is loosened, but not removed. The band retaining spring is compressed and the band is slid forward and off the stock.

STEP 5

The handguard is now lifted off the stock.

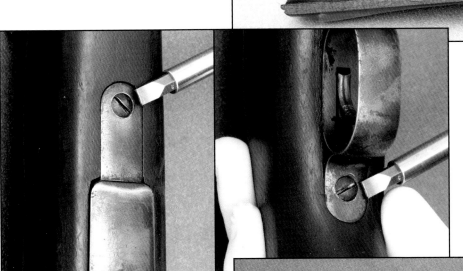

STEP 6

The screws at the front of the magazine and the rear of the triggerguard are removed.

STEP 7

The magazine housing, with floorplate, follower spring and follower still attached, is released from the underside of the stock. The barreled action is also lifted out.

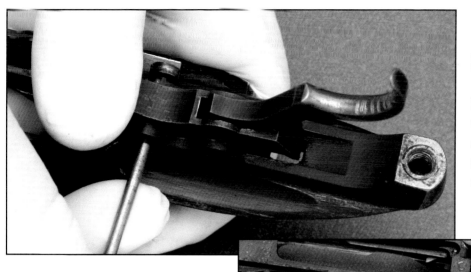

STEP 8

The trigger is easily removed by pressing out its retaining pin while holding down the trigger spring. The pin is not a press fit and should come out with minimal hand pressure.

STEP 9

The trigger and its retaining pin removed from the action.

STEP 10

The floorplate can be released from the magazine by pressing the tab (see arrow). With the rifle assembled, it would be released by pressing in its catch with a punch or the nose of a bullet in the same fashion as seen on the M1898 Mauser.

STEP 11

The follower spring is removed from the floorplate by simply slipping it out of its slots.

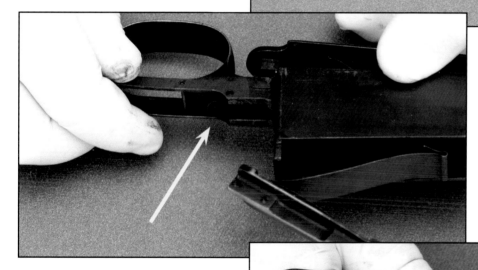

STEP 12

The rear sling swivel is removed by taking out the two
wood screws that retain it.

STEP 13

The buttplate can be removed
by taking out the wood screw
indicated in the photo on the
right and the similar screw in the
tang on the top of the butt. Note
the hinged door in the buttplate,
which is open here to show the
original oiler contained in the butt
trap.

August 1918 Photo of Company
H. 9th Training Regiment coming in from an eight-mile hike at
Plattsburg, NY — the location of
the officer's training facility. The
soldier indicated with an arrow
is Archie Roosevelt, son of the
former President.

'03 Springfield Bolt

Disassembly:

The bolt as it comes out of the rifle. Note that the safety is in the 12 o'clock position.

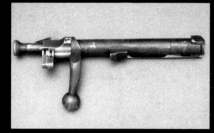

The bolt sleeve lock (see arrow) is pressed in.

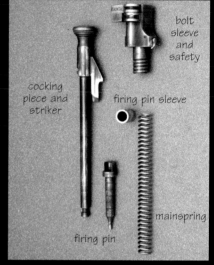

With the firing pin and the striker separated, the bolt comes apart readily.

cocking piece and striker

bolt sleeve and safety

firing pin sleeve

firing pin

mainspring

The bolt sleeve is unscrewed from the bolt body. The cocking piece, firing pin/striker and mainspring come off with it.

Reassembly Notes:

The striker, with its knurled knob, is slipped into the bolt sleeve and the mainspring is slipped over the end of the striker.

In Mauser fashion, the extractor is removed from the bolt body by turning it until its head comes out of its groove. It is then pushed forward and off with a thumb.

The knurled knob is placed against a block of wood, the mainspring is compressed with the sleeve in place and the firing pin is reattached.

Holding the cocking piece in one hand, the safety is flipped over into the "ready" position. Care is needed because this will cause the firing pin to snap forward.

Holding the bolt sleeve in one hand, the knurled knob is pulled back to compress the mainspring while the safety is flipped back into the 12 o'clock position.

The knurled cocking knob is now placed against a block of wood, the sleeve on the striker pulled down and the firing pin taken off.

The firing pin/striker, cocking piece and bolt sleeve are now screwed into the bolt body until the bolt sleeve lock engages. The bolt is now ready to return to the rifle.

Portuguese M1904
Mauser-Vergueiro

STEP 1

With the rifle pointed in a safe direction, it is ensured that it is unloaded and that its magazine is empty.

For this disassembly, we have chosen the converted Portuguese Model 1904/39, which has an upgrade of the cartridge from 6.5x58R to 7.92x57 and a reduction of the barrel and forestock length. This is the most common configuration of this weapon encountered today.

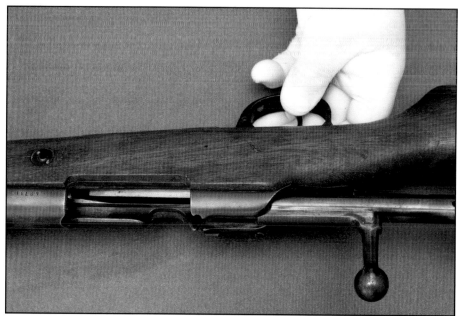

STEP 2

With the bolt stop held open, the bolt is drawn to the rear and out of the rifle.

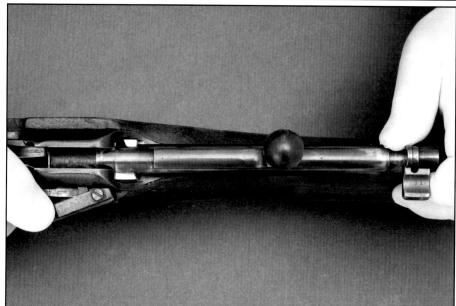

STEP 3

The cleaning rod is unscrewed and pulled out of the rifle.

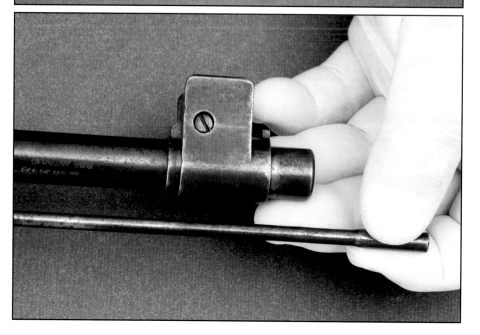

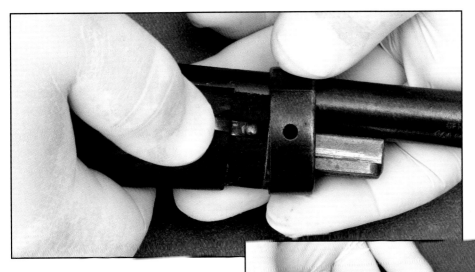

STEP 4

The front barrel band is removed by compressing its retaining spring and pulling the band forward. It will not fit over the front sight, so it is left out of the way, near the muzzle.

STEP 5

The rear barrel band is removed in a similar fashion.

STEP 6

The large screw at the front of the rear sight is removed. It isn't immediately apparent, but this screw actually secures the handguard.

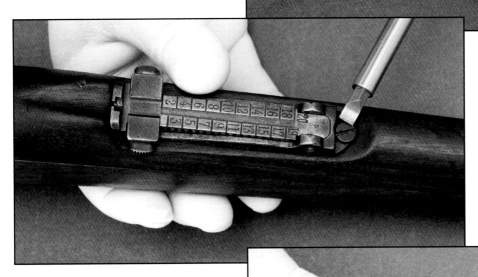

STEP 7

The rear sight is held up. The handguard is pulled forward, up and is turned to clear the wide part of the rear sight. Note the little inlet in the wood where the rear sight screw held the handguard in place (see arrow).

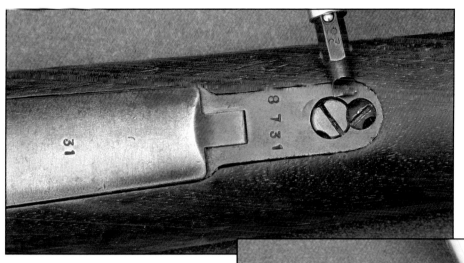

STEP 8

The large screw at the front of the magazine has three half-moon cuts in its head, which allow it to be secured with a smaller lock screw. The small lock screw is removed first.

STEP 9

The large screw can now be taken out. There is an identical screw set-up at the rear of the triggerguard. These are also taken out (no photos shown).

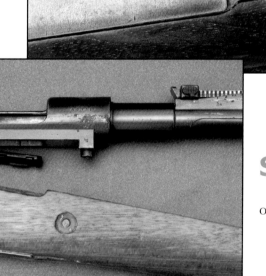

STEP 10

The barreled action is lifted out of the stock.

STEP 11

The floorplate is released by pressing the knurled button inside the triggerguard. It should pop right off. It does not separate from the magazine housing, but stays in place on a hinge. This is different from most other Mausers where this part actually comes off.

STEP 12

The magazine follower and spring can be removed from the floorplate by pulling the end of the spring (a tongue shape) out of its slot.

STEP 13

The triggerguard and magazine housing are pulled away from the stock.

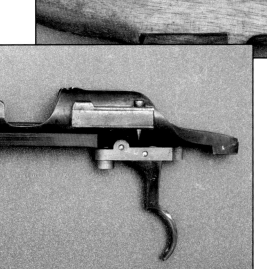

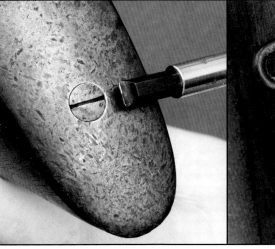

STEP 14

The bolt stop and trigger are identical to the standard Model 1898 Mauser design, and are covered more elaborately in the sections of this book devoted to that rifle.

STEP 15

The buttplate is removed by taking out two screws. The rear sling swivel can also be removed by taking out its two screws.

The Vergueiro Bolt

Disassembly:

The Vergueiro bolt as it comes out of the rifle. This bolt has a bad reputation for being difficult to reassemble, but there is only one tough step.

The cocking piece is rotated toward the bolt handle, relieving tension on the mainspring. This view shows it half way there.

The bolt head is rotated 1/4 turn so that its slotted lug aligns with the solid lug on the bolt body (see inset for a close look at the correct position). The cocking piece can now be slipped off the bolt.

The safety is removed from the cocking piece by turning it 180 degrees to the "safe" position and pulling it straight out.

(left) The bolt head is twisted counterclockwise until it springs out of the bolt body with the firing pin and mainspring. (right) The bolt head and the spring are removed from the firing pin.

Reassembly:

The mainspring is slipped onto the firing pin.

The bolt head slides over the flat end of the firing pin. Note the position of the lug (see arrow). The bolt head will only go on one way.

(left) The bolt head is pushed into the bolt body with the slotted lug aligned with the rib on the bolt body. (right) It is rotated 1/4 turn until it stops. This is the position where it stops.

Rib on bolt body.

(inset, top left) The safety is slipped into the cocking piece and then rotated to the "off" position shown in the picture. (main view) The cocking piece is slipped over the firing pin and into place as shown.

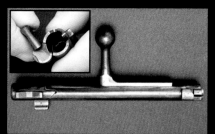

The bolt head is rotated away from the direction of the bolt handle (the only way it will go) 1/4 turn until it is in the position shown in the photo.

This is the hard part. The cocking piece is pulled out. Then the cocking piece and the bolt head are simultaneously turned together until the slot in the bolt head lines up with the slot in the bolt body. The correct position is shown in the last photo and enlarged inset. The bolt handle must be held still to accomplish this. It can be held in a padded vice or in a wood block as shown.

Wood block with hole in it is clamped to the bench.

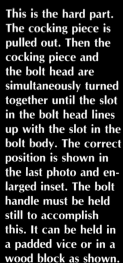

Italian Vetterli
Rifles & Carbines

STEP 1

There are a wide variety of Italian Vetterlis, some with no magazine system, some with Vitali magazines, and others that have been converted to 6.5mm Carcano. Because they are most plentiful for today's collectors, we have chosen to disassemble a Model 1870/87/15 of WWI vintage. Peculiar features of other varieties will be covered later in this section.

First, we confirm that the rifle is not loaded.

STEP 2

The knurled locking ring is rotated by its center button until its notch lines up with the protruding tip of the sliding key that retains the bolt.

STEP 3

With the tip of a screwdriver, the sliding key is pushed through to its furthest position. This key is not meant to be completely removed, only pushed far enough so that it does not impede the progress of the bolt. The bolt is then pulled straight out and set aside.

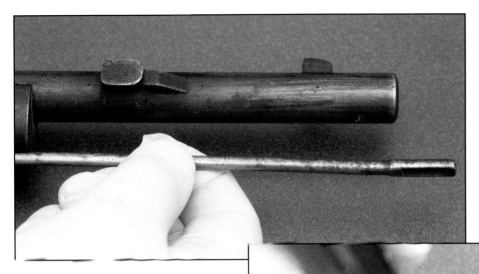

STEP 4

The loading rod is removed. It is threaded on the end and might be screwed into a threaded nut at the end of its channel.

STEP 5

The barrel band screws are loosened. These screws are not intended to be removed completely. The forward barrel band is shown here, but there is also another one further to the rear.

STEP 6

The barrel band retaining springs are compressed, and the two barrel bands are carefully slid off the stock, taking care not to damage the wood.

STEP 7

Starting at the front of the magazine, the three screws on the magazine/triggerguard assembly are loosened, but not removed.

STEP 8

Once all three screws are loosened, they are removed in this order: rear, center, front.

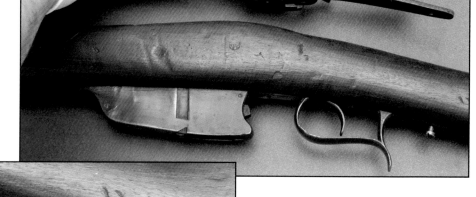

STEP 9

The barreled action can be removed from the stock. This usually does not require any force at all.

STEP 10

The triggerguard assembly can now be removed. This piece is often tight and requires gentle and careful loosening by light taps with a plastic hammer.

STEP 11

The triggerguard assembly can now be disassembled by removing the three slotted screws. However, there is rarely a reason to take this step, as these parts are quite durable and rarely break or fall into disrepair.

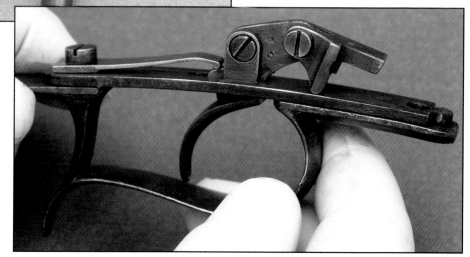

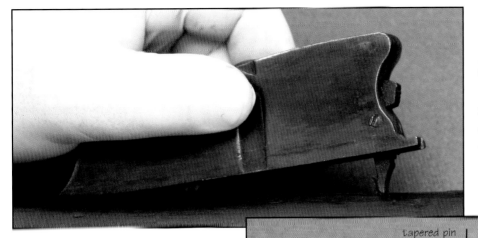

STEP 12

The magazine can now be removed. It should come right out with no special technique or force.

STEP 13

In the unlikely event that the bolt rail requires removal, it is retained by a tapered pin that must be driven out towards the location where the bolt handle was.

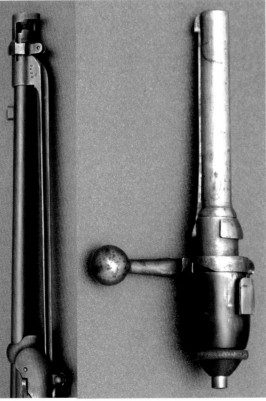

Other Kinds of Italian Vetterlis

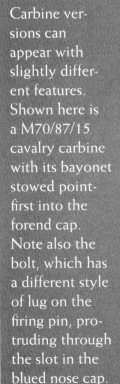

Carbine versions can appear with slightly different features. Shown here is a M70/87/15 cavalry carbine with its bayonet stowed point-first into the forend cap. Note also the bolt, which has a different style of lug on the firing pin, protruding through the slot in the blued nose cap.

Unaltered M1870 versions have no magazine and rotating bolt cover.

Vitali conversions (called M70/87s) have the same magazine as found on the Beaumont disassembled in this book. Also, note one of two springs found on this variation.

Italian Vetterli Bolt

Disassembly:

The knurled spring-retaining nut (at the end of the nose cap) is unscrewed and removed.

The firing pin/striker is withdrawn. The Italian Vetterli used center-fire ammunition, so this is a one-piece unit even though the Swiss Vetterli (a rimfire) was a two-piece unit.

With the nut un-screwed, the nose cap and spring are re-moved and set aside.

The bolt handle is pulled to the rear and removed. The extrac-tor comes off exactly as on the Swiss Vet-terli, which is illustrat-ed on page 68.

spring

retaining nut

nose cap

bolt body and extractor

firing pin/striker

bolt handle

STEP 1

The Lebel that we chose for disassembly is a Model 1886/93 R35 carbine. Many collectors assume that the crude, black finish is not an original military finish. However, they would be incorrect. This painted-on coating was intended for use in France's tropical colonies. Many of these carbines apparently saw service in North Africa during the Second World War.

First, we confirm that the rifle and its magazine are not loaded.

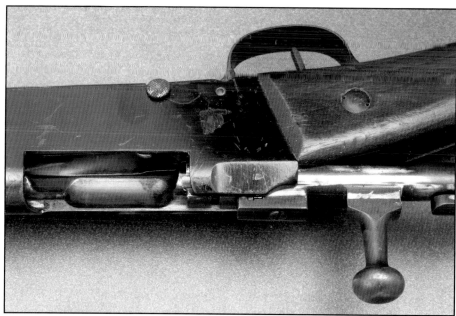

STEP 2

With the bolt handle raised, the screw in the top of the large lug is removed.

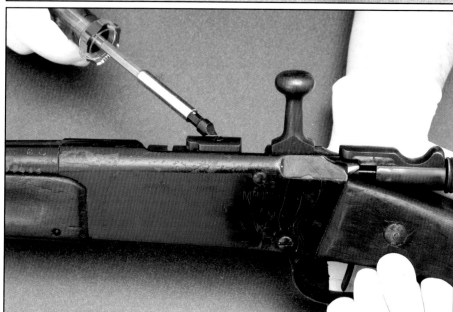

STEP 3

The bolt head is then rotated down, releasing it from the bolt body. When the interlocking parts are clear of each other, the bolt head is pulled forward and off the bolt body.

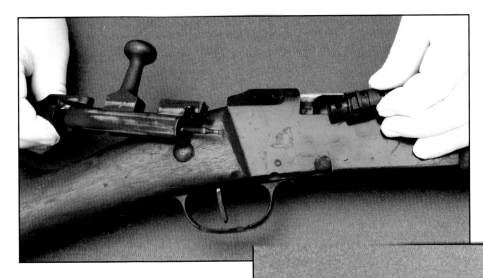

STEP 4

The bolt body is pulled back and out of the receiver while the bolt head is lifted out.

STEP 5

The nosecap and barrel band are removed by depressing their retaining springs and sliding them forward over the front sight.

STEP 6

The pin that passes through the forend at the front of the action is drifted out.

STEP 7

If the magazine cut-off is in the position shown at the right, it is moved backward towards the triggerguard.

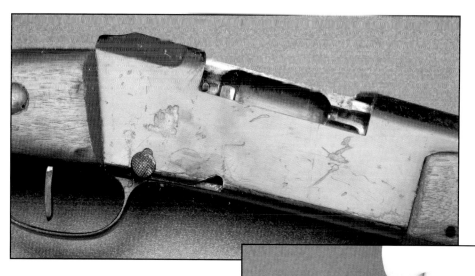

STEP 8

The magazine cut-off lever must be in the position shown at the left in order to remove the forend.

STEP 9

Using a finger, the cartridge carrier is pushed down, exposing the end of the magazine tube.

STEP 10

The forend is removed by using a finger to press in the magazine plunger and pulling the forend down so that it unhooks from the action.

STEP 11

The large screw on the left of the action is now removed. This may be difficult and occasionally it is necessary to drift it out. If this is the case, it is essential to make sure that all of the threads are clear of the hole or the screw and action can be damaged.

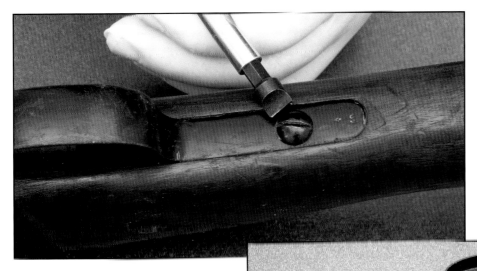

STEP 12

The screw at the rear of the triggerguard is removed.

STEP 13

The trigger and magazine cut-off assembly is pulled down from the rear so that it unhooks from the action. This assembly was not designed to be disassembled readily.

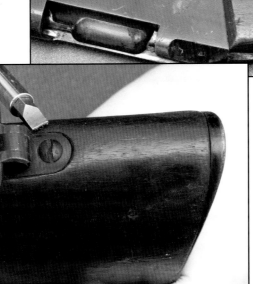

STEP 14

The rear sling swivel can be removed by taking out the two wood screws that retain it.

STEP 15

Likewise, the buttplate can be removed by taking out its screws.

The Lebel Bolt

Disassembly:

The Lebel bolt as it comes out, partially disassembled in order to remove it from the rifle.

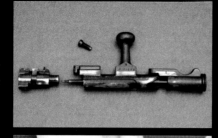

The cocking piece is rotated 1/4 turn in order to relieve pressure on the mainspring.

The knurled nut is turned so that its slot aligns with the mark on the cocking piece (see inset).
With the pin against a piece of wood, the cocking piece is depressed and the knurled nut slipped off the striker.

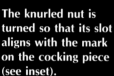

The cocking piece now falls away from the bolt body.

The mainspring and firing pin/striker are slipped out of the front of the bolt body.

The bolt disassembled. We chose not to remove the extractor from the bolt head.

nut   bolt head   cocking piece

firing pin/ striker and mainspring   bolt body

Reassembly:

The mainspring and firing pin/striker are slipped into the bolt body.

The cocking piece is positioned on the end of the bolt as shown and then pushed flush against the bolt body.

With the tip of the firing pin against a block of wood, the cocking piece is depressed and the knurled nut slipped on to the striker. See inset for alignment.

The cocking piece is pulled back and rotated 1/4 turn to return it to the cocked position.

The bolt head is inserted into the receiver and the remainder of the bolt slipped in from the rear. The bolt goes over the firing pin/striker and the bolt head is rotated up. It is shown here half-way to its locked position.

When the bolt head has fully engaged the bolt body, the retaining screw is returned to its hole and the bolt is fully reassembled.

French Berthier
Model 1916

STEP 1

After making certain that the rifle is not loaded, the bolt is turned up, opened, and the screw in the lug connecting the two pieces of the bolt is taken out.

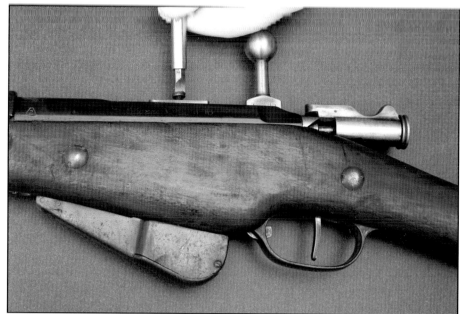

STEP 2

With the screw removed, the head of the bolt is rotated down so that the rectangular projection (see arrow) clears the slot. The rear of the bolt is withdrawn from the rifle and the front section is lifted out.

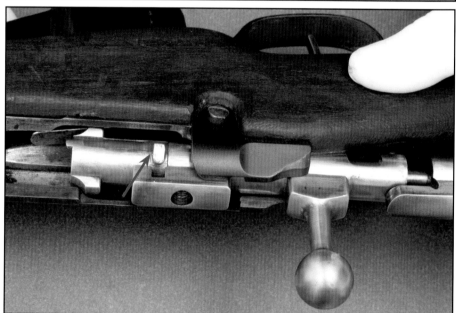

STEP 3

The nose cap and barrel band are removed by depressing their retaining springs and slipping them off the muzzle end of the rifle.

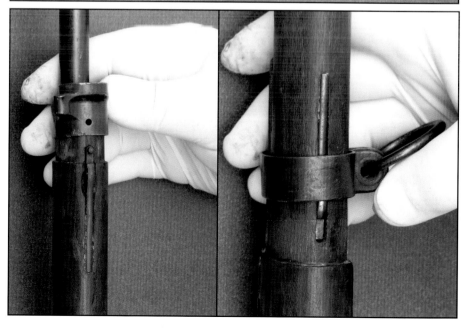

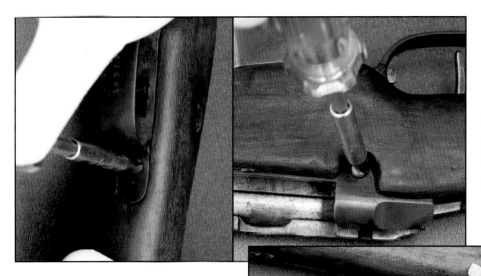

STEP 4

The screw at the rear of the triggerguard is removed (left photo) as well as the screw on the right hand side of the receiver (right photo).

STEP 5

The entire trigger and magazine assembly is now free to be pulled down and out of the rifle. Note that it is rarely necessary to dismantle this assembly further, but that this can be done by removing the screws and drifting out its pins (inset).

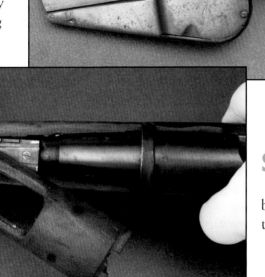

STEP 6

The handguard is removed by pulling it slightly forward and twisting it to avoid the rear sight.

STEP 7

The screw that retains the tail end of the receiver (and which was covered by the triggerguard) is now removed. The barrel and receiver are now lifted from the stock and the disassembly is complete.

M1916 Berthier Bolt

Disassembly:

The Model 1916 Berthier's bolt as it appears after being removed from the rifle as described in the previous steps.

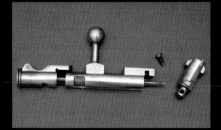

The cocking piece is rotated in the direction of the bolt handle in order to relieve tension on the mainspring.

The slot on the end of the bolt is lined up with the mark on the cocking piece.

In this position, the firing pin is placed against a block of wood and the cocking piece pushed down exposing the end of the firing pin. The nut on the end of the firing pin, which looks like a big screw head, but isn't, is slipped off horizontally.

The cocking piece now falls off and the mainspring and firing pin are withdrawn.

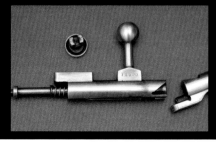

With the exception of the extractor, the bolt is now fully disassembled.

firing pin/striker · mainspring · nut · bolt head · cocking piece · bolt body

Reassembly Notes:

The mainspring is slipped onto the firing pin and both pieces are inserted into the bolt body.

The cocking piece is lined up with the rear of the bolt body as shown.

Using a block of wood, the mainspring is now compressed and the nut returned to the end of the firing pin. With this done, the cocking piece is rotated in the direction of the bolt handle to return it to the cocked position. It is now re-inserted in the rear of the receiver.

The bolt head is laid in the receiver and the two parts pushed together. The bolt head is then rotated upward to re-engage its rectangular projection and the screw that holds the two pieces together replaced.

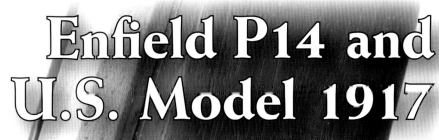

Enfield P14 and U.S. Model 1917

The Enfield P14 and the U.S. Model 1917 are essentially the same rifle. Minor differences include caliber, sights, and details of the magazine and bolt head — none of which, to our knowledge, have an effect upon disassembly. The rifle chosen as our model is a P14 from the collection of John Wall. A M1917 from the collection of Ernest Potter will also be examined for comparison at the end of this section.

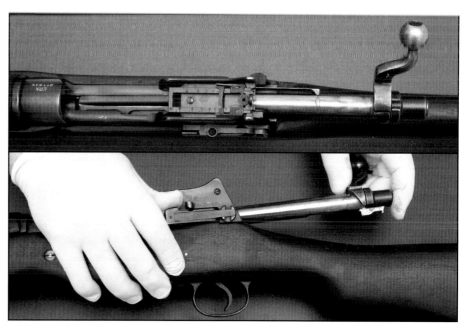

STEP 1

After making certain that the rifle is not loaded and the magazine is empty (top photo), the bolt is removed by holding open the Mauser-style bolt stop and pulling the bolt directly back (bottom photo).

STEP 2

The screw retaining the nose-cap is removed (left view) as is the screw retaining the barrel band (right view). Both the nosecap and the barrel band are then slid forward and off of the stock. Since the front sight would have to be removed to take them off entirely, they are left out of the way near the muzzle end of the barrel.

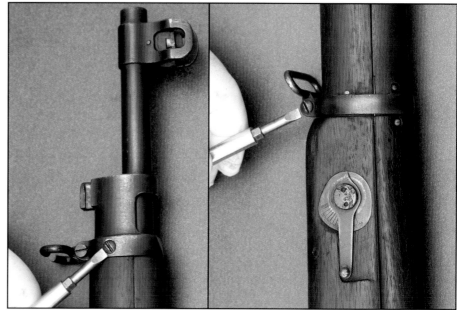

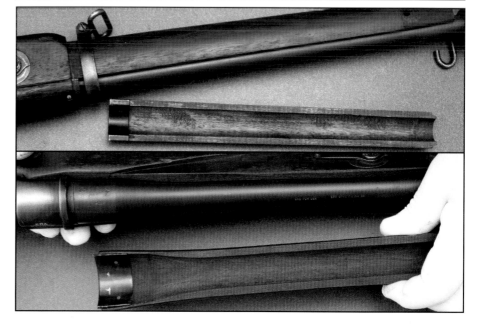

STEP 3

Both the front and rear hand-guards can now be taken off of the barrel and set aside.

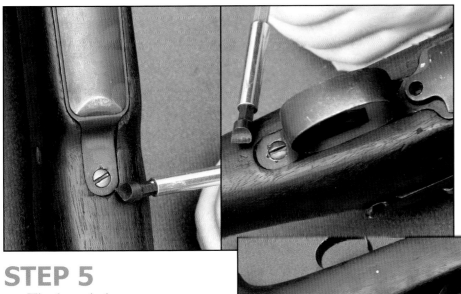

STEP 4

The screw at the front of the magazine is removed (see photo at left). Then the screw at the rear of the triggerguard is removed (see photo at right).

STEP 5

The barreled action is now lifted from the stock. The bolt stop can be dismantled by removing the Mauser-style pointed screw that retains it. In the case of the P14 (but not the M1917), the volley sight would have to be lifted to access it. Note also that it is sharp and potentially dangerous.

STEP 6

The magazine floorplate is removed by pushing a drift or other tool into the hole as shown. The plate is then pushed towards the triggerguard so that it pops out.

STEP 7

The triggerguard is lifted out of the stock and the buttplate removed by unscrewing its screws. The rifle is now disassembled to its basic components.

After a quick look at the U.S. Model 1917 on the next two pages, we will disassemble the Enfield P14 bolt.

A Closer Look at the U.S. Model 1917

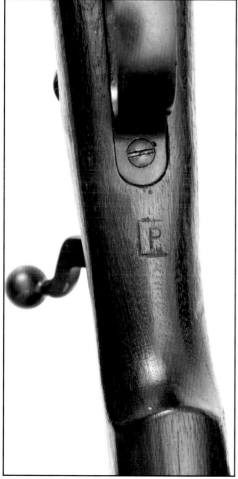

The P14 Bolt

Disassembly:

The bolt, as it comes out of the rifle. Note the Mauser-style extractor, which we have chosen not to dismantle, comes apart exactly as depicted in the Model 1898 Mauser section.

The cocking piece is held back under pressure as shown.

With the cocking piece held back, the firing pin assembly (bolt sleeve, spring, etc.) is unscrewed from the bolt body.

The firing pin assembly is now withdrawn from the body of the bolt.

With the tip of the firing pin pressed against a block of wood, the bolt sleeve is pushed down so that the mainspring is compressed, exposing the cocking piece as shown.

The cocking piece is removed by turning it 1/4 turn in either direction and pulling it up and off.

The spring is now slid off of the firing pin and the bolt is disassembled, with the exception of the extractor, as explained earlier.

firing pin/ striker — bolt body — cocking piece — bolt sleeve — mainspring

Reassembly Notes:

The spring is returned to the firing pin and both are then inserted into the bolt sleeve. Note the flat area on the firing pin. There is a corresponding flat area inside the bolt sleeve.

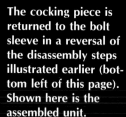

The cocking piece is returned to the bolt sleeve in a reversal of the disassembly steps illustrated earlier (bottom left of this page). Shown here is the assembled unit.

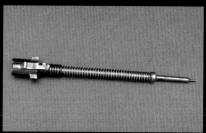

The firing pin assembly is screwed into the bolt body. Once the threads catch and it starts to tighten, it becomes necessary to pull out the cocking piece once with each rotation in order to clear the bolt handle. This is repeated until it can't be turned any further. This completes bolt reassembly.

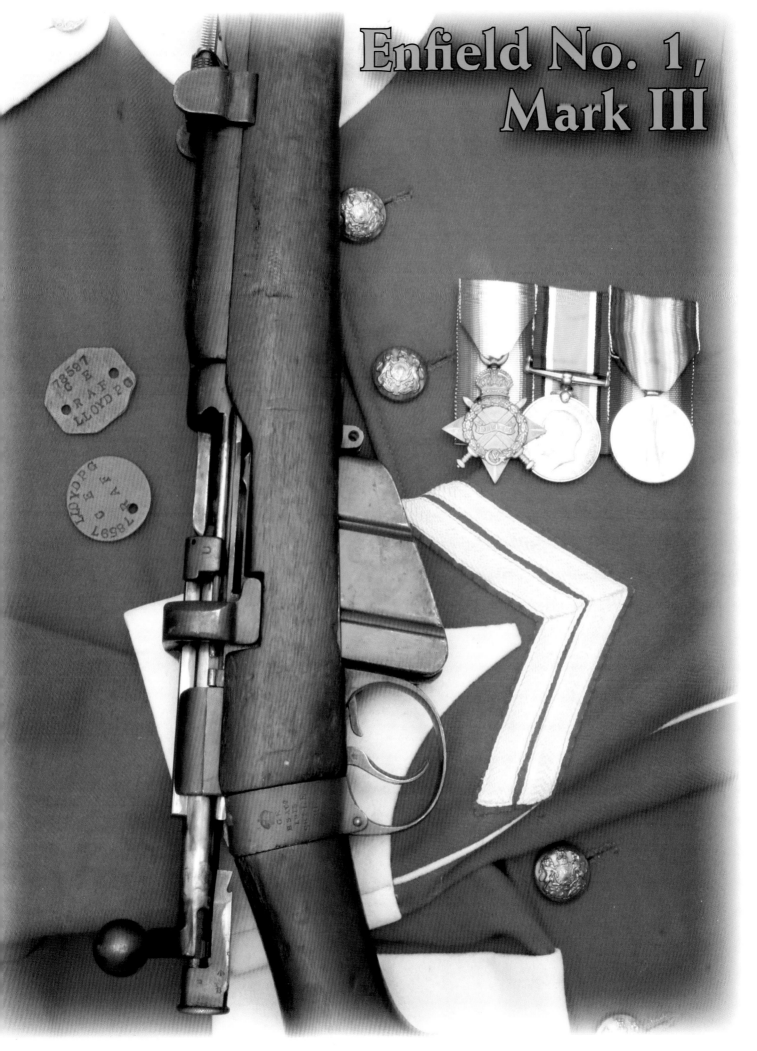

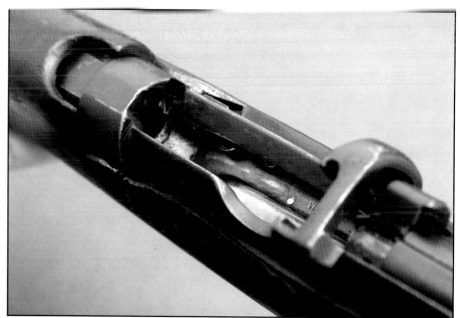

STEP 1

First, we ensure that the rifle is not loaded.

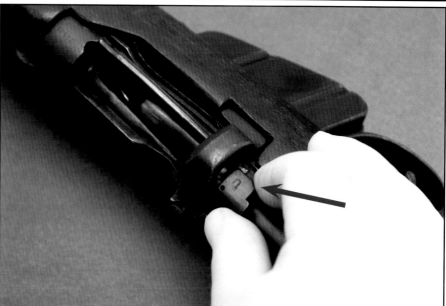

STEP 2

The bolt is opened and pulled back as far as it will go. The bolt head lug (marked U) is pushed up. This can require some force as it is retained by a small spring.

STEP 3

With the bolt head lug in its unlocked position, the bolt is now withdrawn completely.

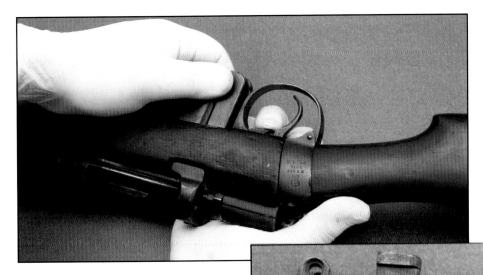

STEP 4

With the magazine release lever depressed (see middle finger of right hand), the magazine is removed.

STEP 5

The forward retaining screw on the nose cap/front sight protector is removed.

STEP 6

The rear retaining screw on the nose cap/front sight protector is removed.

STEP 7

The nose cap/front sight protector slides off of the stock.

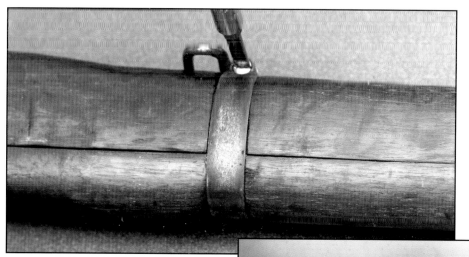

STEP 8

The screw in the barrel band is removed. On most rifles, this screw is just loosened, but here we take it out entirely.

STEP 9

The barrel band is removed using its integral hinge.

STEP 10

The forward handguard can now be lifted off.

STEP 11

The screw in the forend, directly behind the barrel band recess, is now taken out.

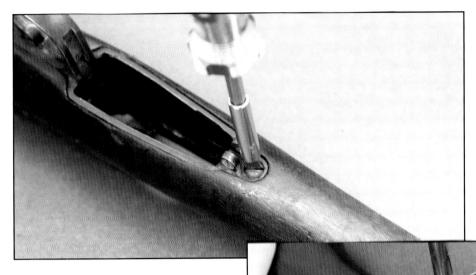

STEP 12
The screw at the front of the magazine housing is removed.

STEP 13
The small screw at the rear of the triggerguard comes out.

STEP 14
The triggerguard and magazine housing now come off of the rifle.

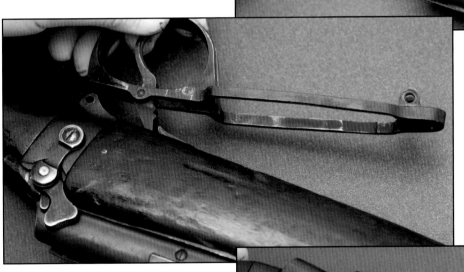

STEP 15
The forestock is removed by gently pulling down at its widest point. It follows the exact angle of the metal collar around the rifle's wrist.

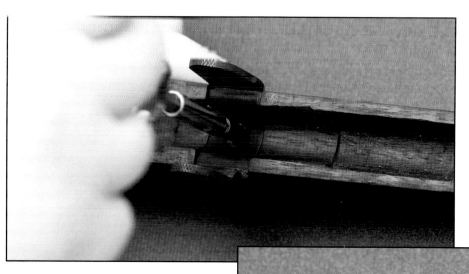

STEP 16

The rear sight protector (the part with the knurled ears) is removed by taking out its screw.

STEP 17

This view shows the rear sight protector, its screw and its nut.

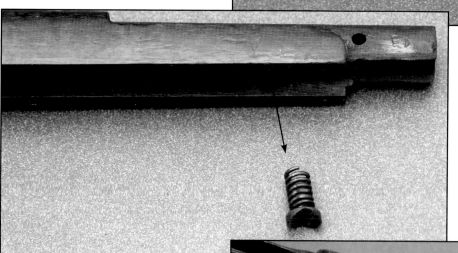

STEP 18

There is a spring-loaded plunger mounted in the forestock's barrel channel that can be removed at this time if necessary.

STEP 19

The rear handguard is removed by pulling it away from the barrel in the direction shown in the photograph.

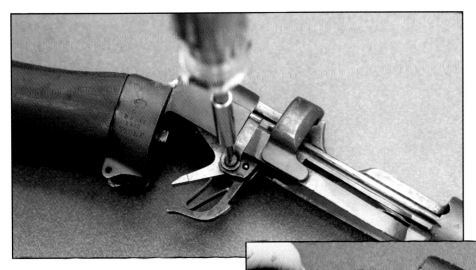

STEP 20

The screw holding the sear and the bolt head retaining spring is loosened (but not taken out).

STEP 21

The sear spring is removed by gently compressing it with a pair of needle-nose pliers.

STEP 22

With the sear spring removed, the screw is lifted out with the bolt head retaining spring.

STEP 23

The sear can now be slipped out and removed.

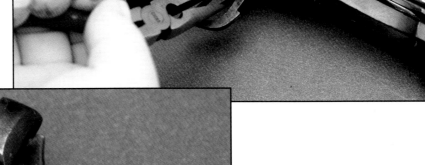

STEP 24

The safety can be removed. Since it is annoying to put back in place properly, this should not be done without good reason.

STEP 25

If the safety is removed, it must be reassembled so that in the "off" position the portion poking though the slot (see arrow in photos) is not obstructing the forward movement of the bolt.

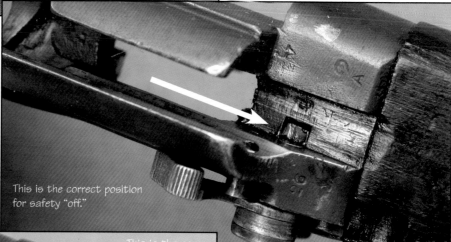

This is the correct position for safety "off."

This is the correct position for safety "on."

STEP 26

This is the incorrect position for reassembly of the safety. This is the safety "on" position, and will prevent the bolt from being inserted.

STEP 27

A view of the safety mechanism removed from the rifle. The little arm (see arrow) moves on a special thread. If this part is removed, it must be carefully reassembled exactly as it came off. Some trial and error may be required before it works properly.

STEP 28

The buttstock can be removed by inserting a long screwdriver into the oiler recess. When the recess is opened as shown here, a long hole is exposed. At the bottom of the hole is a slotted screw head, sometimes covered with a leather washer. Unscrewing this part usually requires considerable force and a quality of screwdriver not found in most workshops.

No. 1, Mark III Bolt

Disassembly:

The bolt head is unscrewed and taken off.

The extractor is mounted in the bolt head with a tiny screw. Unless it is broken, there is no need to remove it.

The cocking piece is pulled back and rotated towards the bolt to relieve pressure on the main spring.

The firing pin locking screw at the rear of the cocking piece is removed. The screw next to it with a half-moon notch missing is the end of the firing pin.

A special tool (Numrich #A1B1A02) is required to remove the firing pin. It is shown here sliding over the firing pin's tip.

Once seated all the way, the tool is cranked to unscrew the firing pin. This will also cause the cocking piece to fall off.

The firing pin and its spring come out of the bolt body. The bolt is now disassembled to its basic component parts.

Reassembly Notes:

Reassembly is basically disassembly reversed. Here the cocking piece is shown being put into place against the bolt body.

With the cocking piece held as shown above, the mainspring and firing pin are inserted and screwed back in using the special tool.

It is important that the half-moon notch at the end of the firing pin lines up with the shape of the locking screw hole. The locking screw is then replaced.

The bolt head is screwed onto the body until the two lugs line up with each other.

The cocking piece is rotated away from the bolt handle to the cocked position in order to reinsert the bolt into the rifle.

Enfield No. 4
Mark I*

STEP 1

It is confirmed that the rifle is unloaded. The bolt handle is lifted, pulled back slightly until it clicks, then pushed forward slightly. The rotating bolt head is positioned to align with the notch cut in the receiver, then rotated up (see the thumb). Next, the bolt is pulled out.

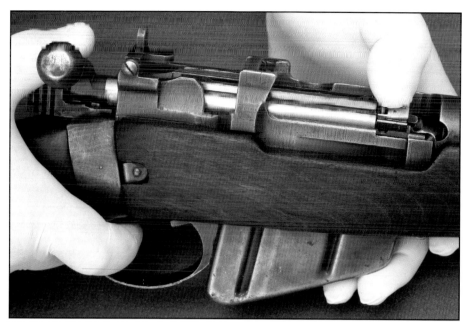

STEP 2

The bayonet is removed by depressing the release button, twisting the bayonet counterclockwise and pulling.

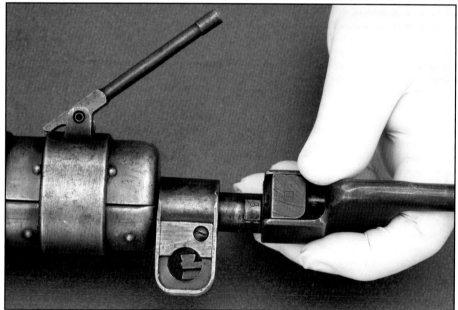

STEP 3

The screw in the foresight protector is taken out. The foresight protector is then removed.

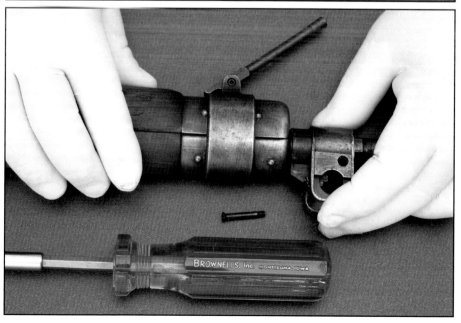

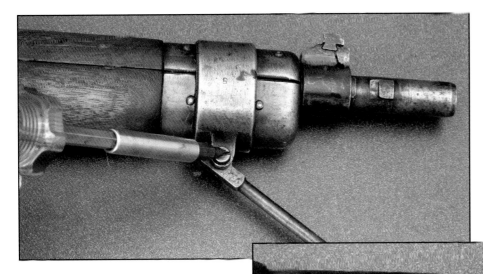

STEP 4

The stacking swivel is removed by taking out its retaining screw. Only Turkish-issued examples of this rifle will have stacking swivels. For other variants of this rifle, this step is skipped.

STEP 5

Once the stacking swivel is removed, the forward barrel band is taken off. Notice that it is held in place by indexing bumps in the metal fore end cap. Some force may be required.

STEP 6

The rear sling swivel screw is removed and the swivel taken off.

STEP 7

The rear barrel band is taken off. It needs to be spread open a bit for it to slide off the stock. Force is sometimes required and there is danger of chipping the wood during this operation.

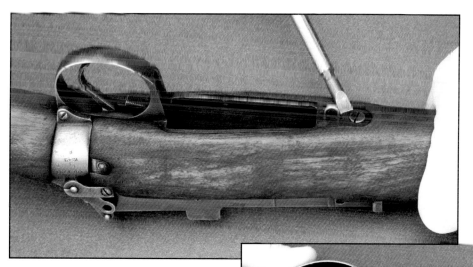

STEP 8

The two handguards arc re moved. The box magazine is also taken off.

Then, the triggerguard screws are taken out (as shown here). There are two of them: a vertical one at the front and a smaller, horizontal one at the rear.

STEP 9

The triggerguard assembly with magazine frame is lifted out. This part is often very tight and can require a couple of light taps with a rubber-headed mallet to knock it free.

STEP 10

The forestock is pushed down and off of the receiver, using diagonal, forward pressure with the thumbs. Some earlier versions of this rifle have an extra screw in the stock, near the metal collar, which has to be removed.

STEP 11

The above procedure can be tricky, and will often require a good deal of patience and some loud profanity before success is achieved.

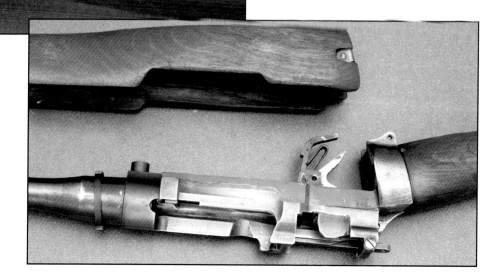

STEP 12

Two large screws free up the buttplate. A deep hole is exposed, with a massive slotted screw at the bottom that holds the buttstock to the receiver. Removing this screw is a real fight, so most disassemblies stop here.

Tanzanian soldiers receiving their SMLE rifles at training camp.

No. 4, Mk. 1* Bolt

Disassembly:

The bolt head is unscrewed and taken off.

The extractor is mounted in the bolt head with a tiny screw. Unless it is broken, there is no need to remove it.

The cocking piece is pulled back and rotated towards the bolt to relieve pressure on the main spring.

The firing pin locking screw at the rear of the cocking piece is removed. The screw next to it with a half-moon notch missing is the end of the firing pin.

A special tool (Numrich #A1B1A02) is required to remove the firing pin. It is shown here sliding over the firing pin's tip.

Once seated all the way, the tool is cranked to unscrew the firing pin. This will also cause the cocking piece to fall off.

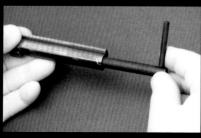

The firing pin and its spring come out of the bolt body. The bolt is now disassembled to its basic component parts.

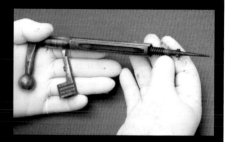

Reassembly Notes:

Reassembly is basically disassembly reversed. Here the cocking piece is shown being put into place against the bolt body.

With the cocking piece held as shown above, the mainspring and firing pin are inserted and screwed back in using the special tool.

It is important that the half-moon notch at the end of the firing pin lines up with the shape of the locking screw hole. The locking screw is then replaced.

The bolt head is screwed onto the body until the two lugs line up with each other.

The cocking piece is rotated away from the bolt handle to the cocked position in order to reinsert the bolt into the rifle.

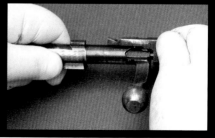

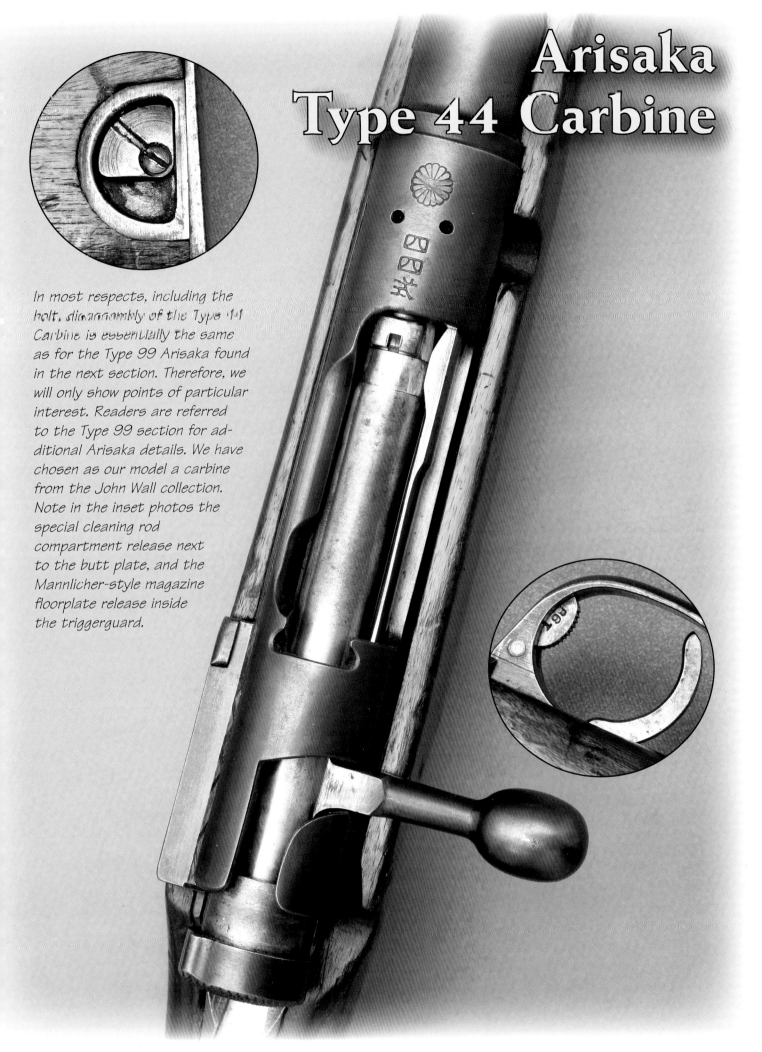

In most respects, including the bolt, disassembly of the Type 44 Carbine is essentially the same as for the Type 99 Arisaka found in the next section. Therefore, we will only show points of particular interest. Readers are referred to the Type 99 section for additional Arisaka details. We have chosen as our model a carbine from the John Wall collection. Note in the inset photos the special cleaning rod compartment release next to the butt plate, and the Mannlicher-style magazine floorplate release inside the triggerguard.

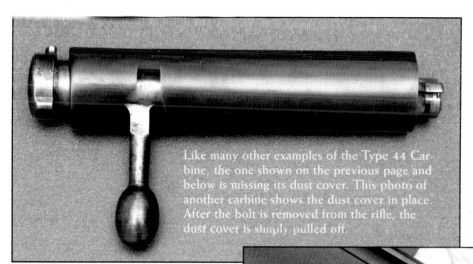

Like many other examples of the Type 44 Carbine, the one shown on the previous page and below is missing its dust cover. This photo of another carbine shows the dust cover in place. After the bolt is removed from the rifle, the dust cover is simply pulled off.

STEP 1

As always, with the carbine pointed in a safe direction, it is ensured that it is not loaded and that the magazine is empty. Understand that these are only notes on special features of this weapon. See the previous page for an explanation.

STEP 2

The unique Japanese nose cap and bayonet assembly is a notable feature of the Type 44 carbine. The bayonet is freed by pressing the knurled button as shown here.

STEP 3

The two screws retaining the bayonet assembly and nosecap are removed. The unit can then be slid off. Note that there are three versions of this nosecap, but that they all disassemble the same.

STEP 4

The barrel band has another unique feature. There are two retaining springs, one on each side (see pressing thumbs). These must be pressed down simultaneously in order to free the band and slide it forward.

Arisaka Type 38 and Type 99 Rifles

STEP 1

For disassembly purposes, the Type 38 and Type 99 rifles are almost identical. We have chosen a Type 99 Rifle for disassembly here.

First, it is ensured that the rifle is not loaded, that the magazine is empty and the barrel is clear. By the way, this is the desirable "Long" version of this rifle, but the basic mechanical design is the same for both Long and Short variations.

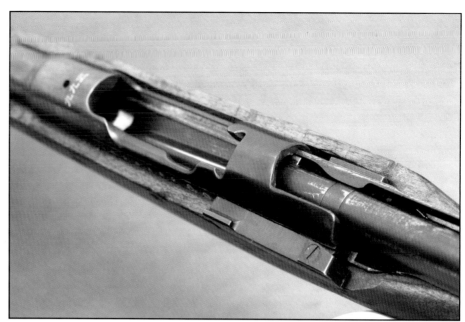

STEP 2

The bolt is removed by turning the bolt handle to its 12 o'clock position (straight up) and drawing the bolt out while pushing out the Mauser-style bolt stop lever.

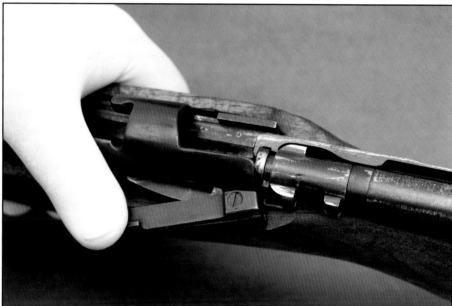

STEP 3

The cleaning rod can be removed. In this case, unfortunately, the cleaning rod would not release from its threads, so it was left in position for the time being.

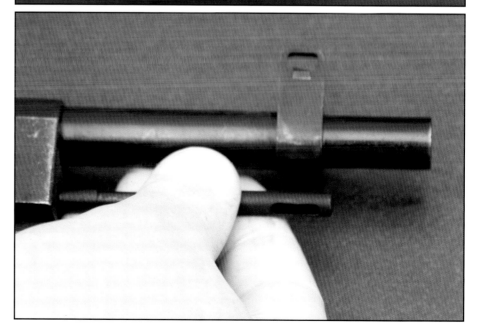

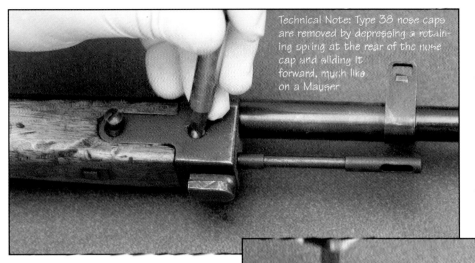

Technical Note: Type 38 nose caps are removed by depressing a retaining spring at the rear of the nose cap and sliding it forward, much like on a Mauser

STEP 4

The two nose cap retaining screws on the right-hand side are removed. Note that there are other nose cap arrangements. Some have two screws while others have none at all. Those with no screws are pinned and peened, which would prevent disassembly except in extreme circumstances.

STEP 5

The one nose cap retaining screw on the left is removed.

STEP 6

The nose cap is still held on by a friction fit and is tapped off gently with a plastic hammer. Note that neither of the barrel bands will fit over the front sight, and only need to be pushed forward all the way towards the muzzle as far as they will go.

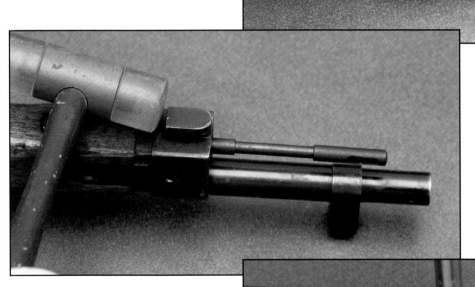

STEP 7

The screw retaining the rear barrel band is removed.

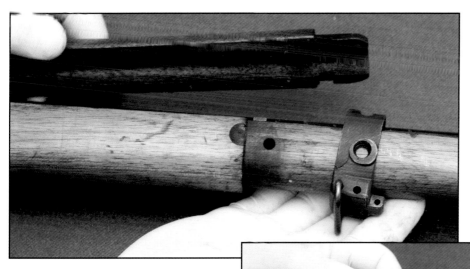

STEP 8

The rear barrel band is slid forward, releasing the handguard, which can now be pulled off. Note that handguards vary and some late stocks have a separate fore end, which is retained by the band.

STEP 9

The floorplate retaining latch (inside the triggerguard) is pulled back, releasing the floorplate. It does not come out, but just springs loose.

STEP 10

The screw at the front of the triggerguard housing is removed.

STEP 11

The screw directly behind the triggerguard is removed.

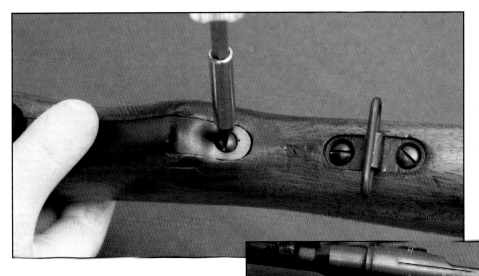

STEP 12

The screw at the rear of the triggerguard tang is removed. Note that the Type 38 rifle and the Type 44 carbine have a separate, lower rear tang.

STEP 13

The barreled action can now be lifted out of the stock.

STEP 14

The triggerguard assembly and magazine are now gently pulled down and out of the stock. This may require some wiggling.

STEP 15

Given the amount of finish on this rifle, we decided not to disassemble the trigger assembly. However, this could easily be done by driving out the pins shown in this photo.

Arisaka Type 99 Bolt

Disassembly:

The cocking piece is pushed in and rotated 90 degrees in the direction away from the bolt handle.

The extractor is slipped on with its slot catching on the projection on the rotating collar and pushed back into place.

When released, it pops right off. Care is taken because it is under spring tension.

The extractor is now rotated until it falls back into the groove along the lip of the bolt head. The single lug behind the groove should be covered by the body of the extractor.

The firing pin/striker and its spring may now be withdrawn.

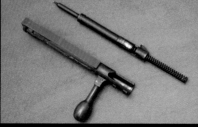

The spring and firing pin are slid into place in the bolt body.

On the bolt head, the extractor is rotated towards the hole (see to the right of the thumb in photo) until it comes out of its notch along the lip of the bolt head.

The lug on the firing pin is oriented as shown in this photo.

The extractor may now be pushed forward and removed.

The cocking piece is pushed in (it will only go in one way), turned 1/4 turn towards the bolt handle and then released.

Reassembly:

The bolt body is oriented as in the photo at right. Note the position of the projection on the rotating collar.

This is what the bolt looks like when properly assembled.

Russian Mosin-Nagant
Rifles and Carbines

STEP 1

Since most Mosin-Nagants disassemble in essentially similar ways, we have chosen what is perhaps the most popular version, the Model 91/30. Other variations will be addressed at the end of this section.

First, we check that the rifle is unloaded, the magazine is empty and the bore is free of obstructions. (Note: This beautiful, laminated-stock rifle appears courtesy of the importers, Century International Arms, www.centuryarms.com.)

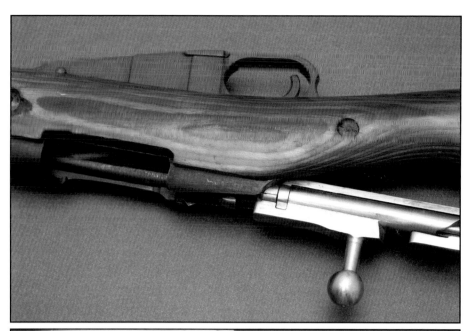

STEP 2

The bolt is removed by rotating the handle up to its 12 o'clock position, holding the trigger down and sliding the bolt to the rear and out of the rifle.

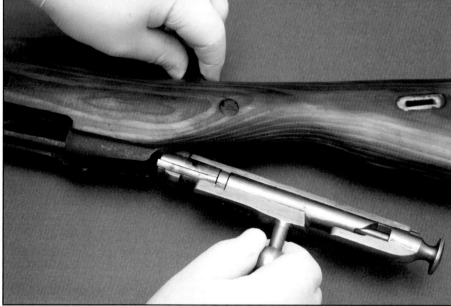

STEP 3

The cleaning rod is removed.

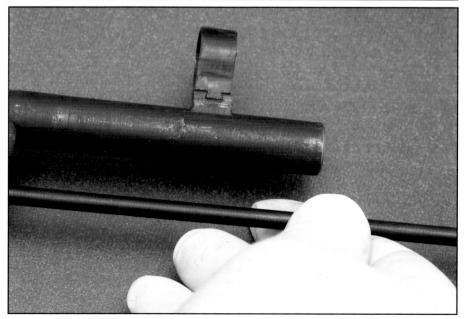

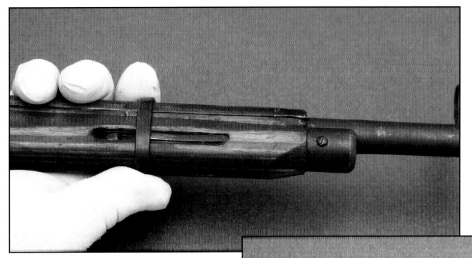

STEP 4

The barrel band springs are depressed so that the two barrel bands can be slid forward. These bands would have to be sprung open to fit over the front sight, but as is shown in the photo below, this is not necessary for further disassembly.

STEP 5

The upper handguard is lifted off.

STEP 6

The screw at the front of the magazine is removed.

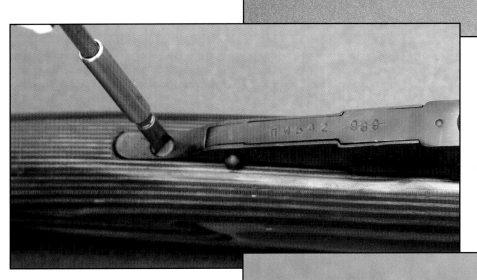

STEP 7

The screw at the rear of the action is removed.

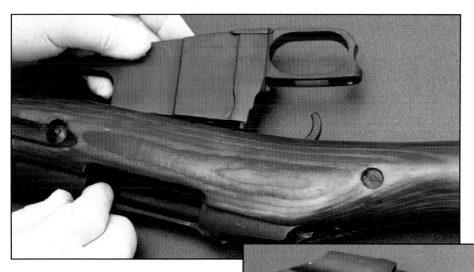

STEP 8
The magazine/triggerguard assembly can now be pulled away from the rifle.

STEP 9
The barreled action is lifted out of the stock.

STEP 10
The trigger spring is removed by unscrewing its retaining screw. The trigger itself is retained by a pin, which should come out with minimal pressure.

STEP 11
This view shows the trigger, spring and pin removed from the action.

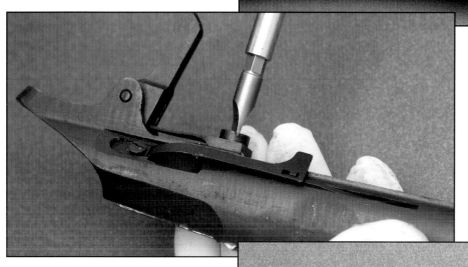

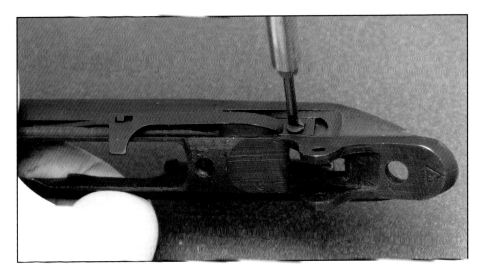

STEP 12

The interrupter and the ejector can be freed by removing the screw on the left side of the action as shown here. The flat area of the ejector, right under the screw, might have to be drifted gently forward to knock it out of its groove.

Other Russian Mosin-Nagants

Disassembly of other Russian Mosin-Nagants, including the carbines, is so similar to the steps shown above that there is little point in treating them separately. A couple of the slight variations that will be encountered are illustrated here.

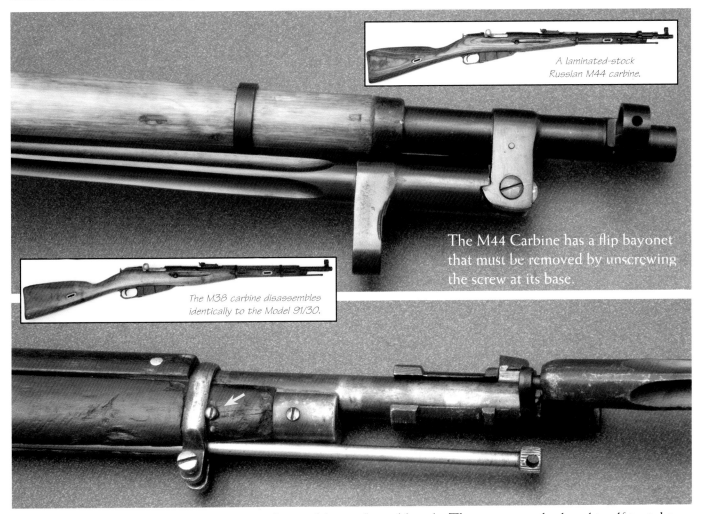

A laminated-stock Russian M44 carbine.

The M44 Carbine has a flip bayonet that must be removed by unscrewing the screw at its base.

The M38 carbine disassembles identically to the Model 91/30.

Model 1891 rifles made pre-1910 can have old-type barrel bands. The screw on the band itself is tightened, which loosens the band to slide forward. Finnish-issued examples have added retaining screws (arrow).

Mosin-Nagant Bolt

Disassembly:

The bolt comes out of the rifle in the cocked position. The bolt handle is grasped in the left hand, and the cocking piece with the right hand.

The cocking piece is rotated up, i.e. counterclockwise, until it stops and tension is relieved on the mainspring. It is not pulled back as part of this action.

The lug on the bottom of the cocking piece should be in the position shown at right once the above step is completed.

The bolt head is now pulled out, turned ninety degrees clockwise, and pulled off.

The firing pin guide is pulled straight off.

The slot at the end of the firing pin guide may be used as a wrench to loosen the firing pin. After the wrench loosens it, the pin can be unscrewed and removed by hand.

Here are the firing pin and its spring being removed as described in the previous step. It is under tension while being unscrewed, requiring some care and attention.

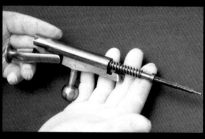

The bolt is now disassembled. Here are the parts. Compared to most other rifles, this bolt has an elegant simplicity. It might not be the slickest action, but it is strong and easy to operate.

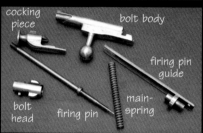

cocking piece · bolt body · firing pin guide · bolt head · firing pin · mainspring

Reassembly Notes:

In general, the disassembly steps are reversed. With the bolt body and cocking piece positioned as shown here, the firing pin and mainspring are screwed in.

The firing pin must be oriented as shown here, with one of its flat sections facing in the direction of the bolt handle, in order to replace the firing pin guide.

The bolt head must be slid on as shown, then rotated to the left.

The bolt head enters the bolt body as shown here. The cocking piece can now be rotated to the cocked position, where disassembly started.

Finnish Mosin-Nagant Models 39, 27 and 24

STEP 1

The Models 39, 27 and 24 disassemble similarly. Since the 39 is more common on the surplus market today, we will use it as our main model. Exceptions for the Models 27 and 24 will be noted at the end of this section.

First, we check that the rifle is unloaded, the magazine is empty and the bore is free of obstructions.

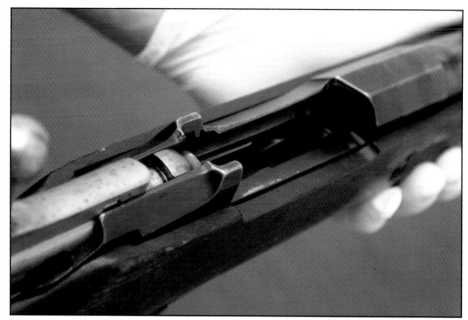

STEP 2

The bolt is removed by rotating the handle up to its 12 o'clock position, holding the trigger down and sliding the bolt to the rear and out of the rifle.

STEP 3

The cleaning rod is removed.

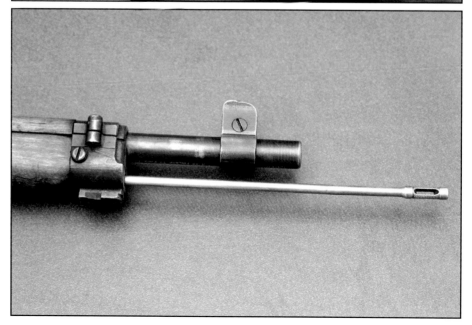

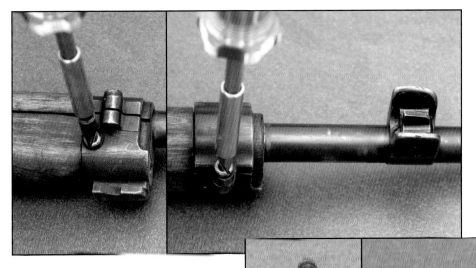

STEP 4

(left) The horizontal front barrel band screw is removed.

(right) The vertical front barrel band screw is loosened. It is a captured screw and does not come out.

STEP 5

(left) The hinge on the front barrel band is lifted.

(right) The front barrel band is pulled down and off of the stock.

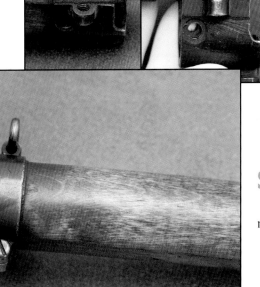

STEP 6

The rear barrel band screw is removed.

STEP 7

The rear barrel band spring is depressed and the band slid forward and off.

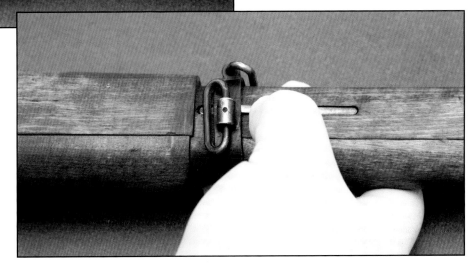

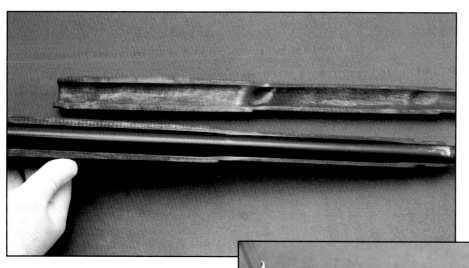

STEP 8

The handguard is removed.

STEP 9

(left) The screw at the front of the magazine is removed.

(right) The screw at the rear of the action is taken out.

STEP 10

The barreled action is now lifted from the stock.

STEP 11

Note that the stock has milled out recesses holding shims and a threaded nut to receive the cleaning rod end. If removed, the shims should be replaced exactly as they came out.

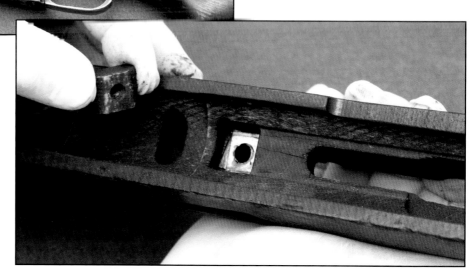

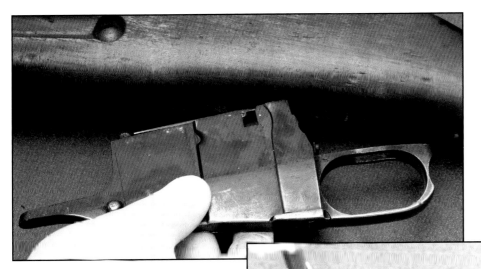

STEP 12

The magazine/triggerguard assembly is pulled down and out of the rifle.

STEP 13

(left) The trigger spring is unscrewed and removed.

(right) The trigger itself is retained by a pin that slides out readily. Note that this trigger is far superior to those found on the unmodified Russian versions of this rifle.

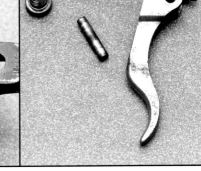

STEP 14

The interrupter and the ejector can be freed by removing the screw on the left side of the action as shown here. The flat area of the ejector right under the screw might have to be drifted gently forward to knock it out of its groove.

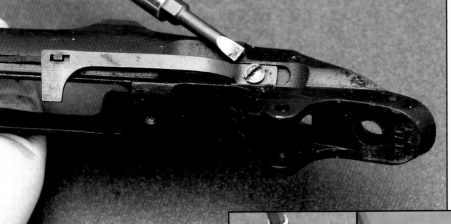

STEP 15

The remaining furniture can now be removed from the stock. For disassembly and reassembly notes on the bolt, refer to the section elsewhere in this book covering the Russian M1891/30 Mosin-Nagant. The bolts are identical.

Finnish Model 24 Exceptions

The Finnish Model 24 Mosin-Nagant differs from the Model 39 primarily in that it retains most of the physical characteristics of the Russian Model 1891 upon which it is built...albeit with a new barrel and recalibrated rear sight. Like the Russian Model 1891 (described in the previous section), the Finnish Model 24 has the old-style barrel bands (but with added retaining screws) and a little retaining screw in the nose cap.

The most distinctive feature of the Finnish Model 24 rifles is that they had replacement barrels, in this case made by the Swiss manufacturer SIG.

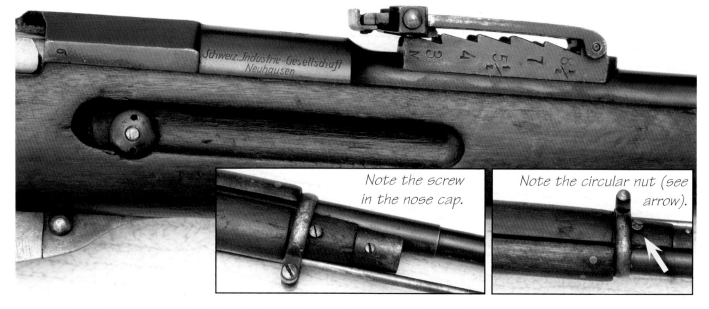

Note the screw in the nose cap.

Note the circular nut (see arrow).

Finnish Model 27 Exceptions

For purposes of disassembly, the Finnish Model 27 Mosin-Nagant differs from the Model 39 primarily in that the hinged nose cap is of a different pattern. It also features a reenforced front sling swivel assembly, which passes through the stock for strength. The rear barrel band is retained by a transverse screw. All of these features are illustrated below and are easily removed with a screw driver.

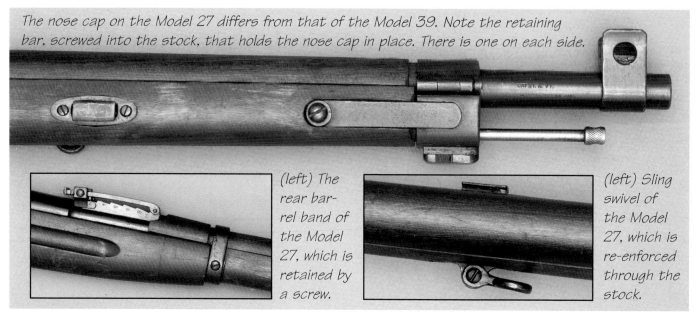

The nose cap on the Model 27 differs from that of the Model 39. Note the retaining bar, screwed into the stock, that holds the nose cap in place. There is one on each side.

(left) The rear barrel band of the Model 27, which is retained by a screw.

(left) Sling swivel of the Model 27, which is re-enforced through the stock.

Swiss K31 Schmidt Rubin Carbine

STEP 1

First, it is ensured that the rifle is not loaded and the magazine is empty. Note that this is a K31 Carbine. There are other models of Schmidt-Rubin that have a significantly different bolt. See the section in this book that deals with those earlier models.

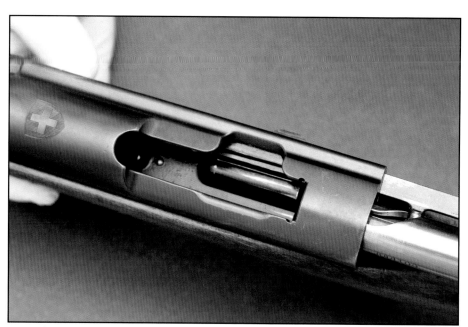

STEP 2

The bolt release lever is depressed and the bolt is pulled straight back and out of the rifle.

STEP 3

The magazine is removed by pressing the serrated magazine release and pulling the magazine out of the rifle.

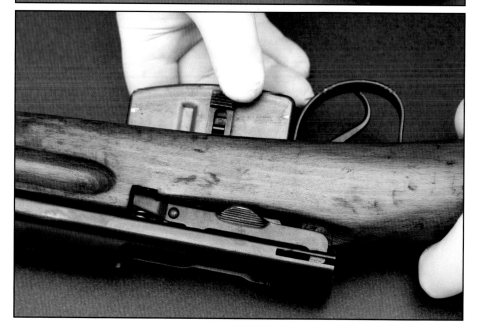

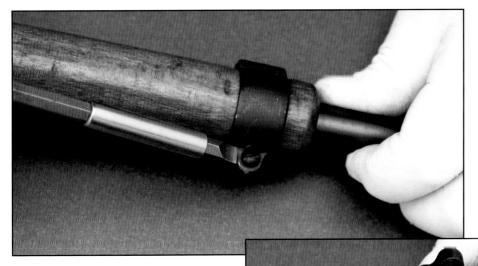

STEP 4

The front barrel band screw is unscrewed all the way.

STEP 5

The top of the hinged barrel band is lifted and the barrel band removed from the rifle.

STEP 6

The rear barrel band screw is removed and the barrel band slid forward and off the rifle.

STEP 7

The handguard is now lifted off. Notice that the serial number is stamped into the wood of the handguard on these rifles.

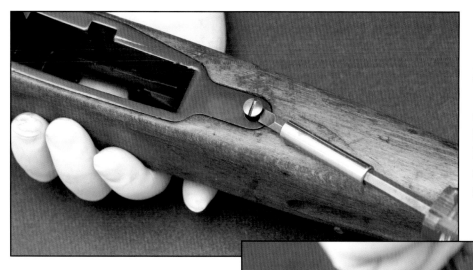

STEP 8

The screw at the front of the triggerguard/magazine assembly is taken out. In this photo, it may look as if the screwdriver is being used to pry the screw up, but this is not intended.

STEP 9

The screw at the rear of the triggerguard/magazine assembly is removed.

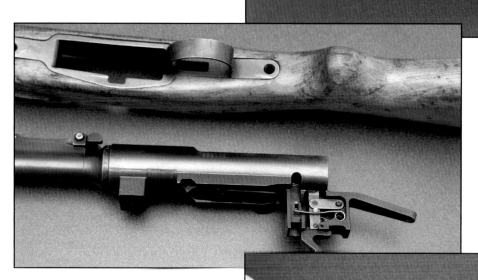

STEP 10

The barreled action is now lifted out of the stock.

STEP 11

The triggerguard/magazine assembly is lifted off the rifle.

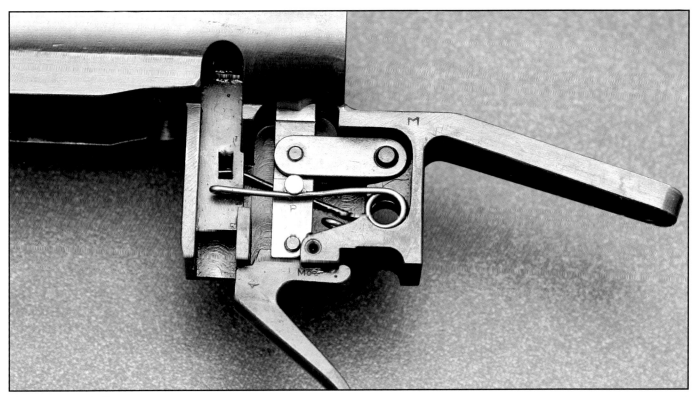

STEP 12

The K31 has a complex and finely tuned trigger, perhaps the most sophisticated ever to appear on a military rifle. It almost never requires service and should only be disassembled by an expert.

STEP 13

The buttplate is removed by taking out the two screws shown. Often, under the buttplate there is a tag indicating the name, unit and hometown of the last soldier to carry this rifle in service. Some collectors have even succeeded in contacting these veterans.

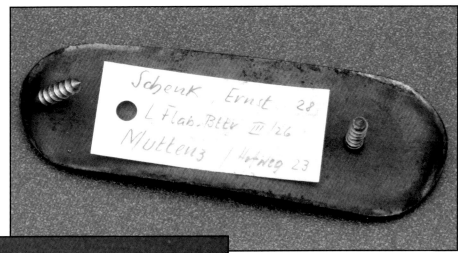

STEP 14

As a last step, the sling bar in the buttstock can be taken out by removing the two screws shown. Note the wear at the bottom of the butt. This is normal and a product of how these rifles were carried in service, partly protected behind backpacks, with the two extreme ends sticking out.

Swiss K31 Bolt

Disassembly:

The cocking piece is pulled back and turned so that the rectangular tab is positioned on the apron (see arrow) as shown.

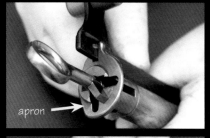

The bolt handle assembly is lifted out of the bolt at the front and slid forward to release it from the apron at the rear.

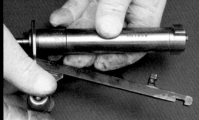

Holding the extractor in place with one finger, the rear of the bolt is turned about 1/4 turn in either direction, and slid out of the bolt body.

The bolt head unit, with its integral extractor, slides out of the bolt sleeve. The two pieces are shown here.

The cocking piece is rotated and allowed to go in so that the rectangular tab falls into the slot shown (see arrow). This releases tension on the spring.

The spring is pulled back with one hand and the firing pin pushed off as shown in the photo.

The cocking piece may now be withdrawn. The bolt is now disassembled with the exception of the extractor, which is not normally removed.

Reassembly Notes:

The bolt head is slipped into the bolt sleeve and oriented so that the slots line up as shown in the photo.

The striker mechanism is reassembled by reversing the disassembly steps, and is then inserted into the bolt sleeve and turned so that it aligns as shown in the photo at the right.

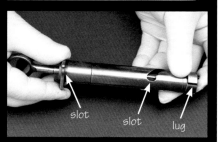

The bolt handle is slid backwards into the slot in the apron, and the tab at its front-end dropped into the central slot in the bolt sleeve.

With the bolt held together with one hand, the cocking piece is pulled out and rotated 1/8 of a turn towards the bolt handle and its rectangular tab dropped into the slot shown in the photo. The photo was taken just as the tab is about to reach its final position. The bolt is now returned to the rifle, holding down the bolt release lever and pushing down the magazine follower.

Earlier Schmidt Rubin Longarms

Note:
For rifle disassembly, refer to the K31 section, which is almost identical. The early bolts, however, will be treated on the next page.

Early Schmidt Bolts

Disassembly:

With the bolt removed from the rifle, the cocking piece is drawn back and rotated so that its rectangular tab rests on the rear of the bolt.

Gently rotating the front half of the bolt sleeve, the bolt handle is now lifted away from the bolt body.

The bolt cap (the rear part of the outer bolt sleeve) is unscrewed from the front half and removed.

The front half of the sleeve will now slide off the bolt body. Note that this is a M1911 bolt. On the M1889 bolt, the locking lugs are located on the opposite end of this piece.

The cocking piece is rotated so that the rectangular tab falls into the slot shown. This releases tension on the spring.

The spring is pulled back with one hand and the firing pin slipped off as shown in the photo.

The cocking piece may now be withdrawn. The bolt is now disassembled with the exception of the extractor, which is not normally removed.

Reassembly Notes:

The striker/firing pin and spring assembly is reassembled by reversing the disassembly steps.

The front half of the bolt sleeve is slipped onto the bolt body as show in the photo.

The striker/firing pin assembly is screwed into the front half of the sleeve. It does not have to be tightened and when complete should be aligned as shown at the right.

The cocking piece is now drawn back and its rectangular tab positioned as in the first step above. The bolt handle is then returned to its slots.

Holding the bolt body and handle with one hand, the cocking piece is rotated so that its tab falls into the slot as shown in the photo. The bolt is now assembled.

STEP 1

It is confirmed that the rifle and magazine are unloaded, but the bolt is closed and remains in the rifle for the first steps of disassembly. It is possible to disassemble the rifle with the bolt removed, but experienced Ross collectors say that this can lead to chipping of the wood.

The example shown here is a Ross Mark II***, but rifle disassembly is just about identical for all other types except the Mark I, which is exceptionally rare.

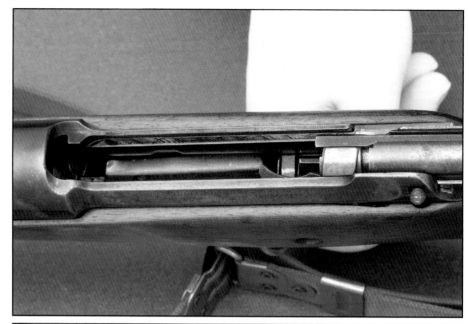

STEP 2

(left) The screw holding the nosecap is removed and the nosecap slid forward as far as it will go. On this rifle, it does not clear the front sight.

(right) The screw holding the rear barrel band is taken out and the band slid forward as far as it will go.

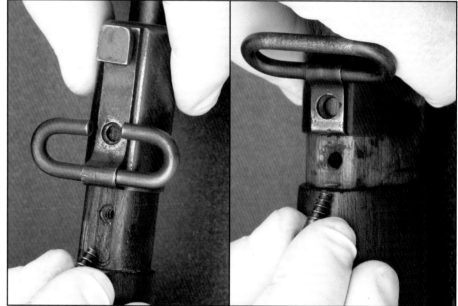

STEP 3

(above) The front handguard is removed by sliding it forward around the rear sight as shown.

(below) The chunky, little rear handguard is removed by lifting it up from the rear. It is retained by spring clips that grab the barrel.

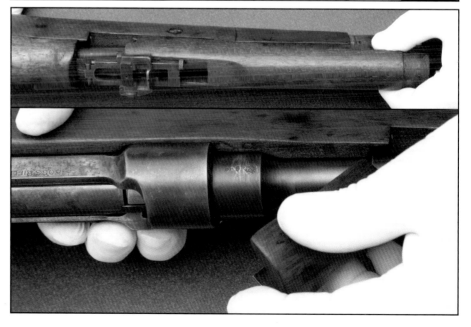

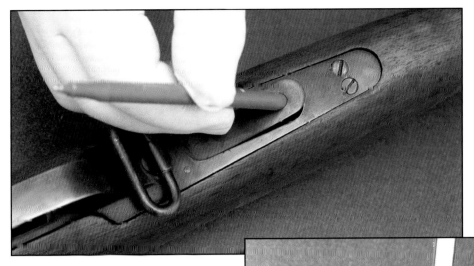

STEP 4
The magazine dustcover is removed by inserting a plastic pen and prying it up as shown while pulling forward.

STEP 5
The rear receiver screw is now removed.

STEP 6
The two screws at the front of the receiver's bottom are taken out.

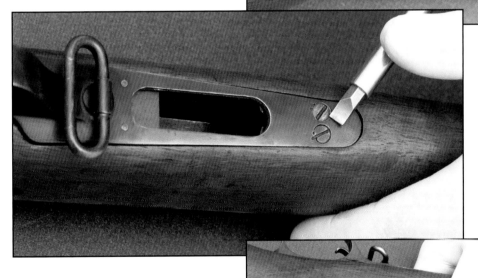

STEP 7
The barreled action pulls out of the stock. The bolt is now removed from the action.

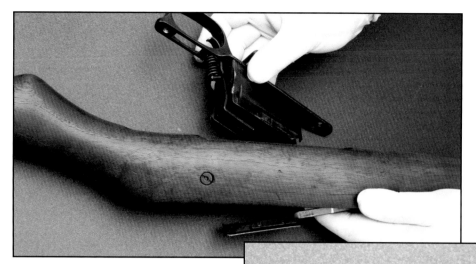

STEP 8

The magazine and trigger-guard come out.

STEP 9

The magazine lifter assembly is now exposed. It is an interesting mechanism and worthy of some extra notice.

STEP 10

The magazine lifter assembly can be taken out by removing this split nut (see arrow), which requires a special tool. These screws originally went through the stock from left to right, but are more often found reversed as shown here.

STEP 11

The magazine cut-off and its spring come apart almost effortlessly.

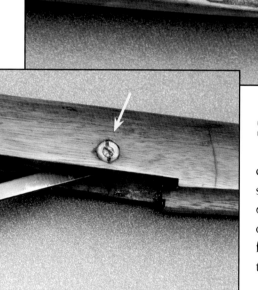

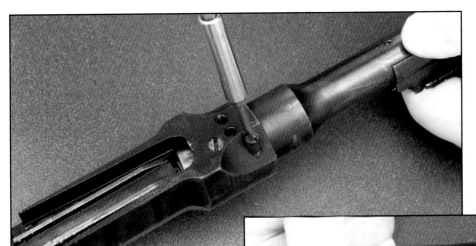

STEP 12

The Ross has an amazing mechanism for separating the barrel from its action. The locking screw (shown) is unscrewed and removed.

STEP 13

The barrel can now be unscrewed by hand. It is a left-hand thread (unscrewed by turning clockwise). Only one-and-a-quarter turns are required.

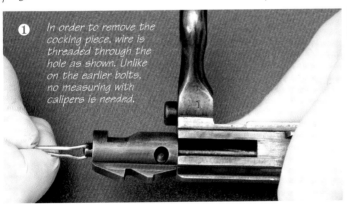

Technical Note: If the barrel will not come off by hand, lubricant and a plastic-headed hammer will usually loosen it.

Ross Bolts with Differences

There are two basic Ross bolts encountered: the Mark II and the Mark III. About 95% of Ross Mark II rifles actually have bolts that disassemble like the Mark III bolt, having been upgraded during WWI. Naturally, all of the Mark III rifles should have the later-type bolt. The full bolt disassembly on the following page shows the unaltered Mark II bolt. Specific differences for the Mark III type are illustrated here.

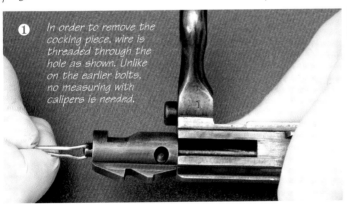

❶ In order to remove the cocking piece, wire is threaded through the hole as shown. Unlike on the earlier bolts, no measuring with calipers is needed.

❷ Next, the wire is pulled, shifting the cocking piece so that needle-nose vise grips can be clamped onto the striker.

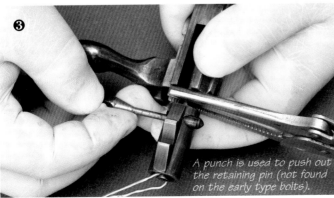

❸ A punch is used to push out the retaining pin (not found on the early type bolts).

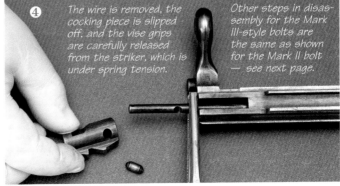

❹ The wire is removed, the cocking piece is slipped off, and the vise grips are carefully released from the striker, which is under spring tension.

Other steps in disassembly for the Mark III-style bolts are the same as shown for the Mark II bolt — see next page.

Ross Mark II Bolt

Disassembly:

The bolt is removed from the rifle by pulling the trigger, pressing the bolt stop on the left side of the action and pulling the bolt straight back.

(left) The relative position of the locking lugs and extractor is noted for reassembly. (right) The extractor is pushed up gently and pulled forward with a screwdriver.

A vernier caliper is used to measure the distance from the end of the firing pin to the end of the cocking piece. This is only necessary on early type bolts where the firing pin does not protrude from the cocking piece.

The cocking piece is pulled out and the unthreaded portion of the firing pin grasped with a pair of needle-nose vise grips.

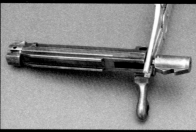

The cocking piece is unscrewed and set aside.

The bolt head and internal sleeve are now turned out of the bolt body.

A special tool is needed to remove the firing pin retaining nut (here made from a piece of 5/16 OD steel automotive brake line with a notch cut in it). The nut, under spring tension, is carefully unscrewed.

The bolt's disassembled internal components.

internal sleeve
mainspring
firing pin
nut   washer

Reassembly Notes:

In reassembling the bolt, it is important that the tiny washer (see arrow) be returned with its projecting tab entering the corresponding notch in the bolt sleeve.

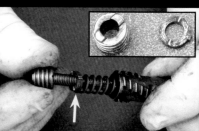

With the spring compressed and washer and nut in place, the special tool is used to tighten the nut. It clicks with each turn.

(left) The assembled internal sleeve is returned to the bolt body and the extractor replaced as shown. (right) Vise grips grasp the firing pin's unthreaded area, allowing the cocking piece to be screwed on.

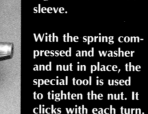
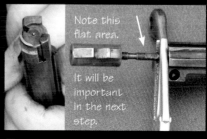

Note this flat area. It will be important in the next step.

The cocking piece is screwed in to the previously measured depth. The button (see arrow) must align with the flat section shown above.

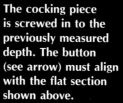
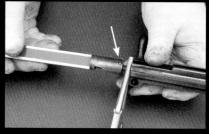

M1 Garand

Rifle courtesy of
Ernest Potter.
Simulated WWII
battle scenes
with thanks to
Allan Cors.

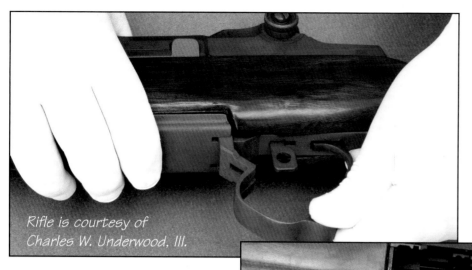

Rifle is courtesy of
Charles W. Underwood, III.

STEP 1

After pointing the rifle in a safe direction and ensuring that it isn't loaded, the bolt is returned to the closed position. Next, the triggerguard is pulled toward the butt to release its catch, and then away from the rifle until it locks open.

STEP 2

The entire trigger assembly lifts out of the rifle as one piece. Since this is a field strip only, the trigger assembly will not be taken apart.

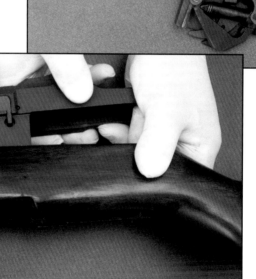

STEP 3

Holding the rear sight, the receiver and barrel (with the handguard attached) are pulled off of the stock, which is set aside.

STEP 4

(top) The follower rod (see arrow) is pulled towards the muzzle and lifted away from the barrel.

(bottom) As can be seen, the compensating spring comes away with the follower rod, and the remainder of the spring is pulled entirely out of its tube.

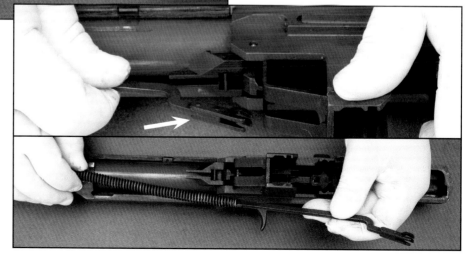

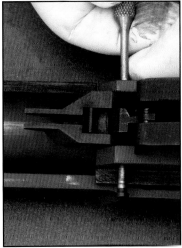 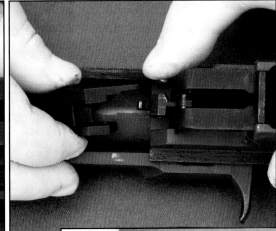

STEP 5

(left) A drift is used to push out the follower arm pin. It only goes one way...you push toward the side with the head on it.

(right) The accelerator is lifted up and out of the rifle.

STEP 6

The follower arm is lifted out. Note how the little pins (see arrow) on the end of the follower arm engage slots in the follower. It is important to observe this arrangement for reassembly.

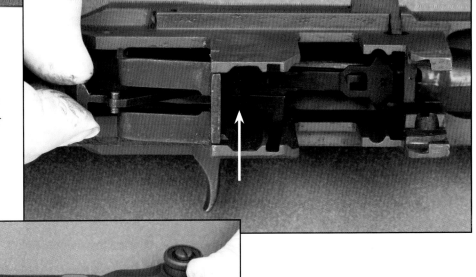

STEP 7

The cartridge guide is pulled up and wiggled out of the magazine housing as shown.

STEP 8

The follower is lifted out of the magazine housing. Gunsmiths do not recommend disassembly of the follower.

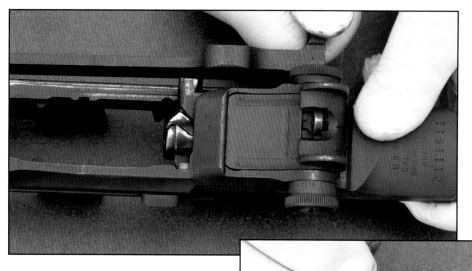

STEP 9

The operating rod is removed by pulling it back and then carefully out, away from the receiver. This piece is easily bent.

STEP 10

The bolt is slid forward in the receiver and slightly twisted until it can be pulled out as shown.

REASSEMBLY HIGHLIGHTS

Reassembly is basically a reversal of the disassembly procedures. The trickiest part is the arrangement of the cartridge guide, the follower arm and the operating rod catch. They are shown here properly assembled.

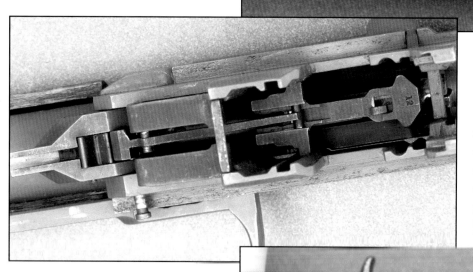

In order to connect the follower rod to the follower arm, it is necessary to lift the follower slightly as shown on the left side of the photo. Note how it slides up in its grooves.

M1 Carbine

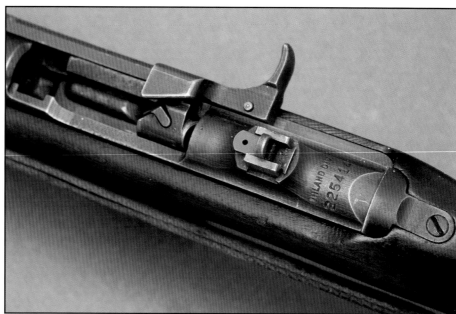

STEP 1

First, it is ensured that the rifle is not loaded and the magazine is empty. This is a WWII production carbine made by Inland.

STEP 2

The magazine release button is pushed and the magazine removed.

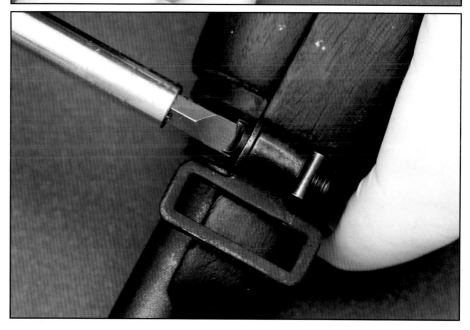

STEP 3

The barrel band screw is removed, along with the sling swivel.

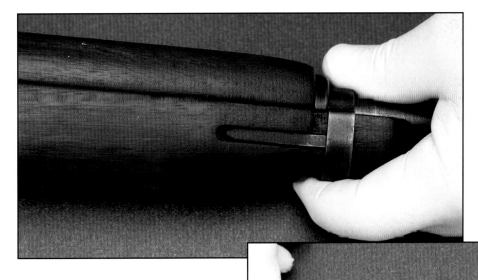

STEP 4

The barrel band spring is compressed and the barrel band slipped forward. It does not clear the front sight and cannot be taken off entirely.

STEP 5

The handguard is lifted off of the barrel.

STEP 6

The complete action can now be taken out of the stock as shown.

STEP 7

The trigger assembly retaining pin is held in place by a tiny spring, so it is necessary to start it by pushing on the end as shown with the blade of a small screwdriver. It is easy to slip and scratch the metal.

STEP 8

The trigger assembly retaining pin is now pulled out.

STEP 9

The trigger assembly is slid backwards, separating it from the action. In this disassembly, we are not going to take apart the trigger assembly.

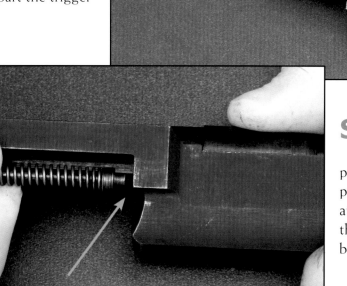

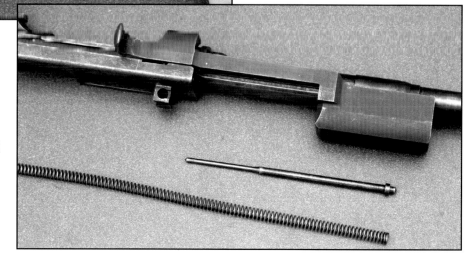

STEP 10

The recoil spring is compressed and the tip of its guide is pulled out of its hole in the operating slide (see arrow). This frees the entire spring, which can then be pulled out of the receiver.

STEP 11

This view shows the receiver and operating slide with the recoil spring guide and recoil spring removed.

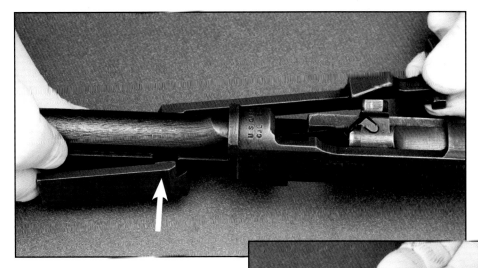

STEP 12

The operating slide is removed from the receiver by moving it so that the notch (see arrow) in the barrel's guide rail lines up with the tab on the inside edge of the operating slide. In this position, the operating slide is pushed down at the front and lifted as shown at the rear.

STEP 13

The bolt is removed by twisting it and lifting it out of the receiver as shown.

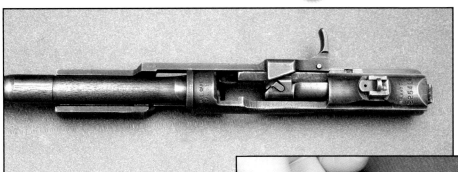

Reassembling the M1 Carbine

STEP 14

The bolt, receiver and operating slide are reassembled by reversing the disassembly steps until they look as shown in the photo. The slide is worked back and forth to ensure free movement.

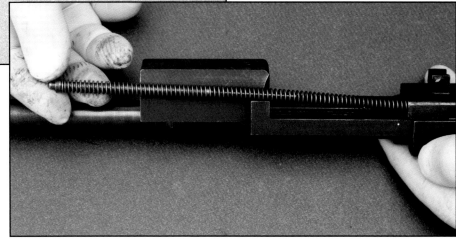

STEP 15

The recoil spring and recoil spring guide are fitted back into the receiver as shown and then compressed until the head of the guide snaps into its hole in the operating slide.

STEP 16

The trigger assembly is slipped back onto the action from the rear until the holes for the retaining pin line up. Note how the thumb (far left in the photo) pushes the trigger assembly's rails into the slots in the receiver.

STEP 17

The trigger assembly is fixed in place by returning its pin as shown. Its little retaining spring will hold it in place when properly seated.

STEP 18

The assembled action is returned to the stock, hooking at the breech as shown.

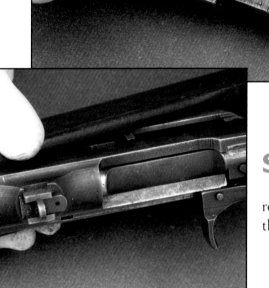

STEP 19

The handguard is returned to place and the barrel band slid backwards to retain it. The barrel band screw is tightened with the sling swivel in place.

French MAS
Model 1936

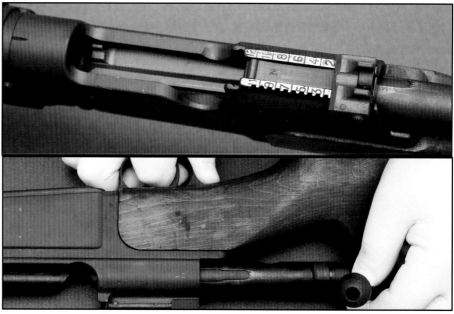

STEP 1

As usual, the first step is to confirm that the rifle and its magazine are not loaded. Next, the bolt is removed by pulling the trigger back while withdrawing the opened bolt as shown. Note that two special tools are required for disassembly. These, however, are easily made with a file and old screwdrivers (see above).

STEP 2

(photo on left) The bayonet is removed by depressing the button, see arrow, and pulling it out.

(photo on right) The floorplate is removed by squeezing the knurled buttons on either side of its front lip as shown. While squeezing, the floorplate is pulled down and then forward.

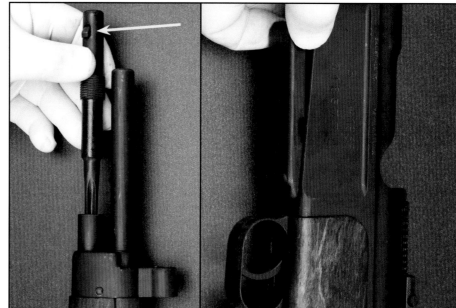

STEP 3

(photo at left) The screw at the rear of the triggerguard is removed.

(photo at right) The triggerguard is pulled forward and off, allowing the buttstock to be pulled down and off the action as shown.

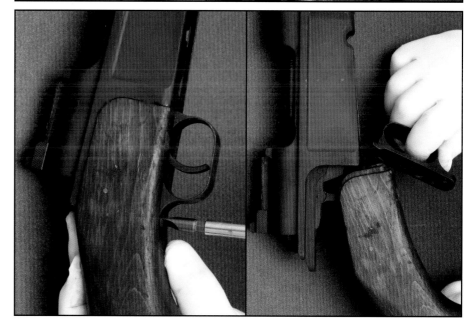

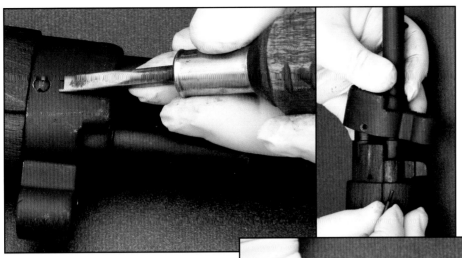

STEP 4

(photo at left) The smaller of the two special tools is used to unscrew the nosecap retaining screw.

(photo at right) The screw is pulled out and the nosecap pulled off over the front sight.

STEP 5

(photo at left) The larger of the special tools is used to remove the screw at the barrel band. The sling swivel is then taken off.

(photo at right) The barrel band is slightly sprung and slipped off of the stock as shown.

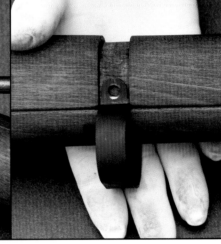

STEP 6

The handguard is now lifted off.

STEP 7

The forend is removed by pulling down from the muzzle end and then unhooking it from the receiver. The hook is indicated in the photo with an arrow.

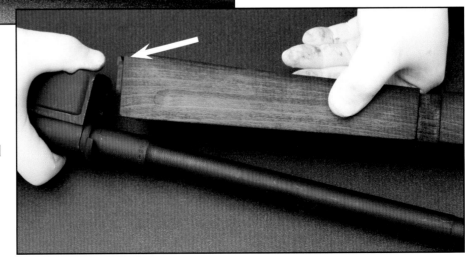

MAS M1936 Bolt

Disassembly:

A view of the bolt as it comes out of the rifle.

The end of the bolt is pushed in with the palm of the hand and rotated away from the bolt handle until it unhooks and pops out.

The bolt end, spring and striker/firing pin will now all slide out of the bolt body as shown here.

The bolt is now disassembled to its major components. Further disassembly is not generally recommended.

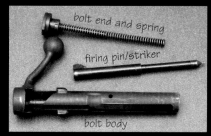

bolt end and spring
firing pin/striker
bolt body

Reassembly:

The striker is slipped into the bolt body. Note the orientation of the lug on the end.

The spring fits into the striker as shown in this photo. Note the orientation of the small lug on the end piece.

The end piece is compressed with the palm of the hand. When it has fully entered the bolt body, it is twisted in the direction of the bolt handle until it stops.

The end of the bolt when assembled looks like this.

The assembled bolt. It is returned to the rifle in the cocked position. Note the position of the lug on the striker (see arrow). This is the only thing that tells you it is cocked.

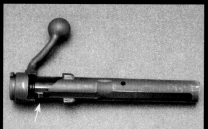

This is a view of the other side of the assembled bolt. Note that there is no way of telling whether this rifle is cocked when the bolt is returned to the rifle.

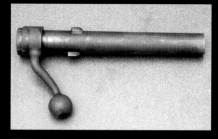

Removing the extractor is not part of a normal disassembly for this kind of bolt. However, if it is absolutely necessary, it can be removed by pressing it up with the blade of a screwdriver to disengage its rear locking lug, and then pulling it off.

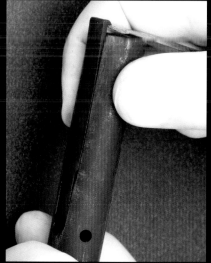

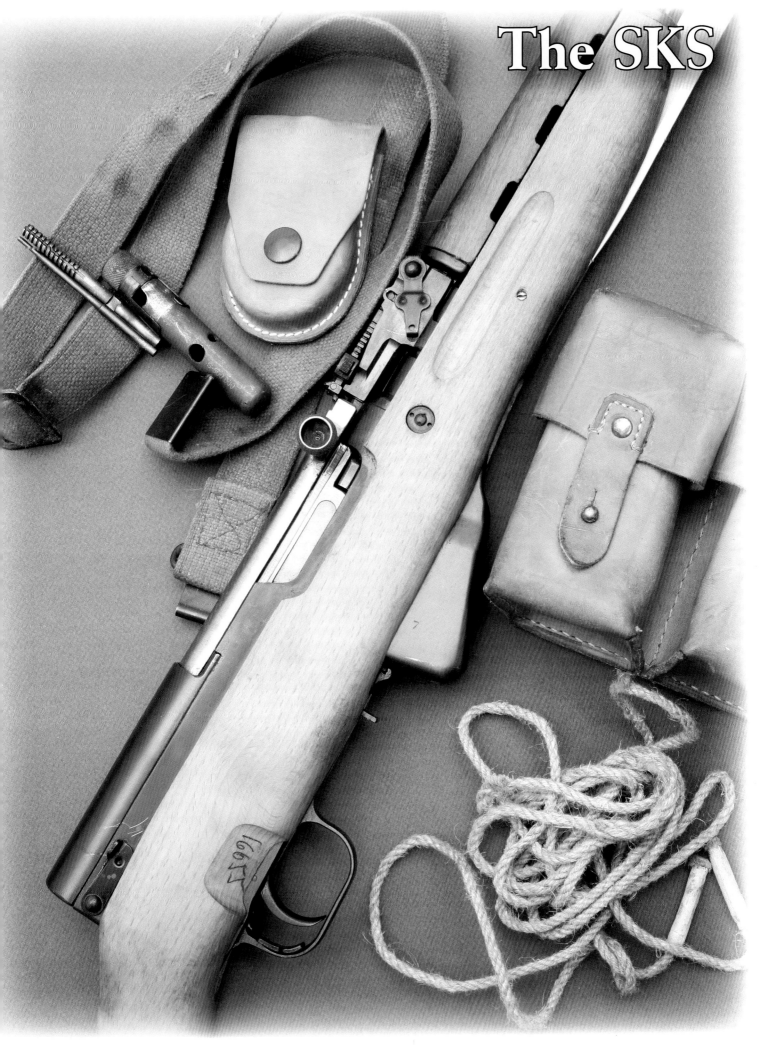

STEP 1

There were many variations of the SKS produced around the world, but for this disassembly we chose a Yugoslavian Model M59, because they are readily available on today's surplus market. Note that the photo on the previous page is of a M59/66A1, which also has an integral grenade launcher with sight. The disassembly rifle appears here courtesy of the importer, Century International Arms, (800) 527-1252, www.centuryarms.com.

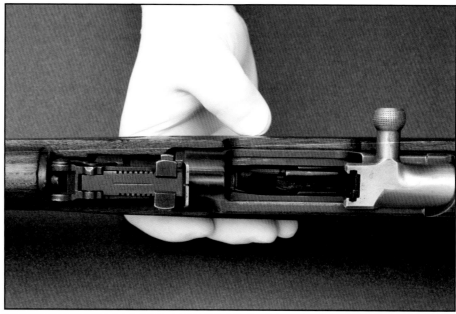

STEP 2

With the muzzle pointed in a safe direction, it is confirmed that the rifle and magazine are unloaded. The safety is then engaged as shown in this photo.

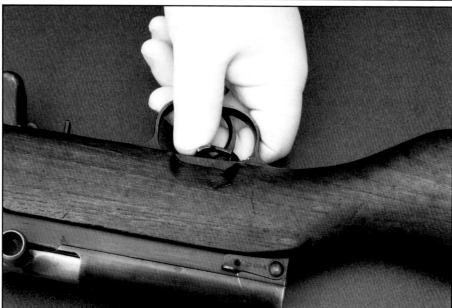

STEP 3

The magazine cover is then released, leaving the magazine open during the disassembly. The bolt is also released carefully so that it snaps forward into its closed position.

STEP 4

The take-down lever at the rear of the receiver is rotated up and pulled out to release the receiver cover. Note that if the bolt has not been returned to its forward position before doing this, the receiver cover will fly off dramatically!

STEP 5

With the receiver cover off, the recoil spring assembly is withdrawn from the bolt and set aside.

STEP 6

The bolt and carrier (loosely together as a unit) are slid to the rear and lifted out of the receiver.

STEP 7

The triggerguard is released by tapping the button shown. The triggerguard springs up when this has been done successfully.

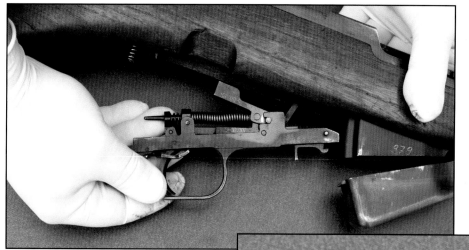

STEP 8

The triggerguard and trigger assembly are removed from the stock by pulling down from their rear as shown.

STEP 9

The gas cylinder tube latch is swung up to the position shown in the photo. Note that it is easy to scratch the rifle's finish doing this.

STEP 10

The gas cylinder and handguard are lifted off the rifle by pulling up from the end near the sight.

STEP 11

The magazine is removed by pulling it down and away from the stock as shown. Note that the front of the magazine engages a slot in the receiver.

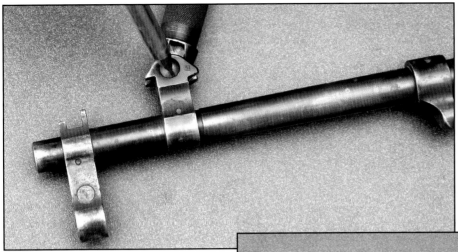

STEP 12

The integral bayonet is removed by unscrewing its retaining screw. Note that its grip is under spring tension.

STEP 13

The receiver and barrel are removed from the stock. This can be a tight fit and gentle tapping from the underside may be necessary.

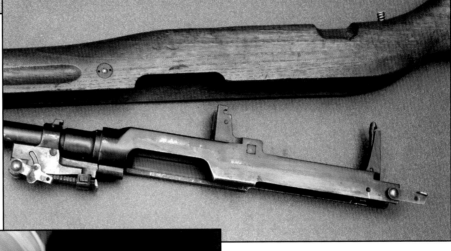

STEP 14

With the tip of the recoil spring assembly protected by a wooden block, the spring is compressed using hand strength and its little keeper at the end slipped off.

STEP 15

(top) The four pieces of the recoil spring assembly.

(bottom) The gas piston extension rod, which is housed in the rear sight, is removed by rotating the latch all the way up (see arrow). The rod is under spring tension and is guided out with the thumb so that it doesn't pop out too energetically.

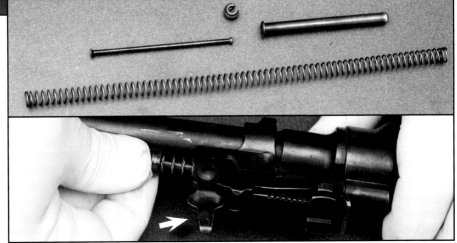

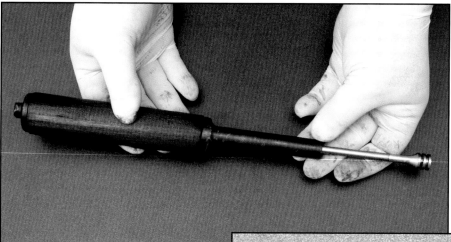

STEP 16

The gas piston slips out of the gas cylinder tube.

STEP 17

The trigger assembly is held together with numerous pins as can be seen here. However, Steve Kehaya, author of *The SKS Carbine* book, recommends that it not be disassembled. If necessary, he suggests cleaning with automotive brake cleaner (spray) followed by immediate relubrication.

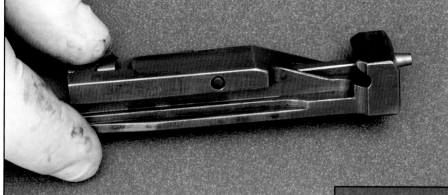

STEP 18

Likewise, the firing pin is held in with a retaining pin, but further disassembly of this unit is rarely necessary. However, it is ensured that the firing pin is moving freely before it is reinserted into the rifle.

REASSEMBLY NOTE:

One tricky part is putting the recoil spring assembly back together. Its parts reassemble easily, but the component that looks like a nail will fall out unless it is retained somehow. A thin metal rod is slid into the assembly as shown and then (with the metal rod against a block of wood) the spring is compressed and the keeper installed to hold it all together. The metal rod is then set aside.

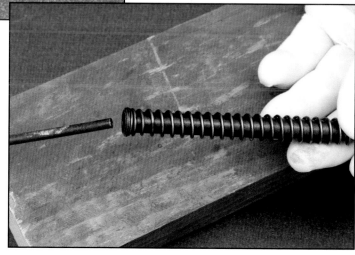

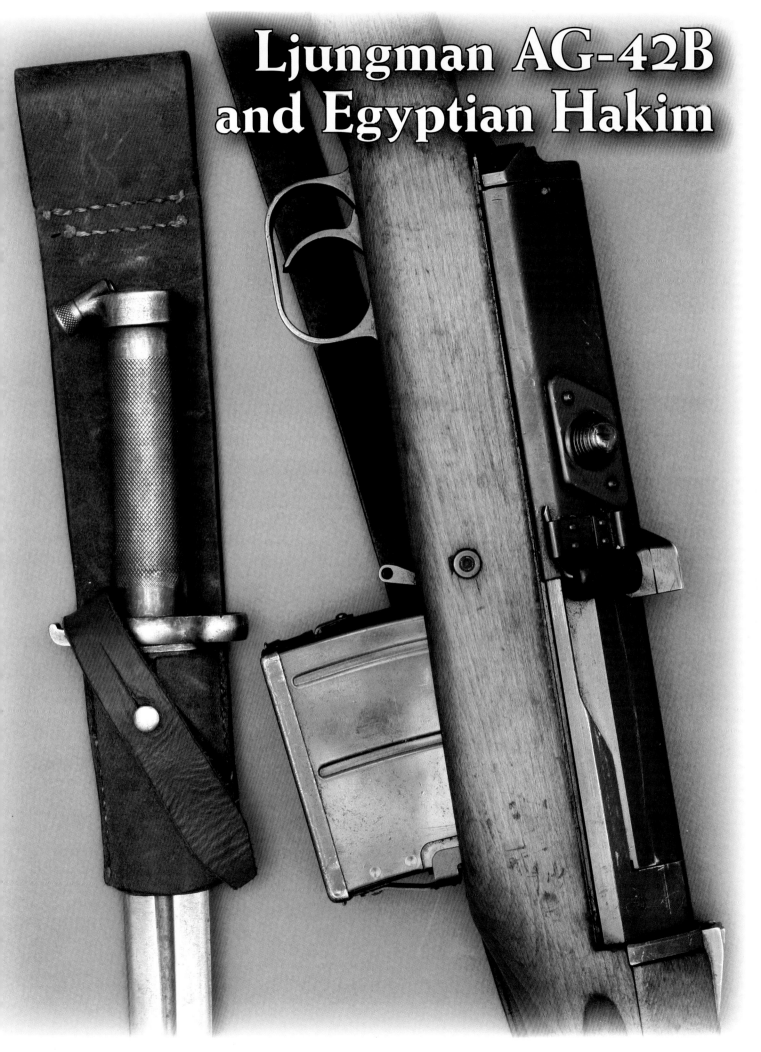

Ljungman AG-42B and Egyptian Hakim

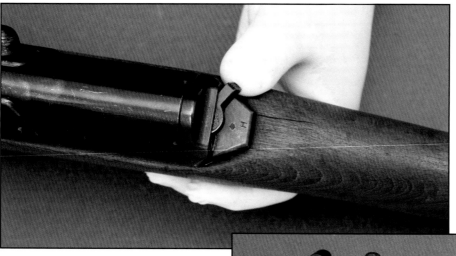

STEP 1

We disassembled the Swedish AG-42B. The Egyptian Hakim is essentially the same with minor differences that we will note as we go along. We have limited ourselves to field stripping the rifle as further disassembly was intended to be done by trained armorers.

First, the safety is moved to the right, i.e. the "safe" position.

STEP 2

The dust cover is then pushed forward until it locks onto the bolt carrier and then pulled back, with the carrier and bolt, to check that the rifle is unloaded and that the magazine is empty.

STEP 3

The magazine is removed by pressing the spring clips on either side and pulling it down. The magazine catch on the Hakim is slightly different (see the section on the Rashid in this book for a look at that style of catch).

STEP 4

The dust cover, bolt carrier and bolt are now pushed forward an inch or two and the safety moved to its middle position, at which point the block at the rear of the receiver is lifted out and off the rifle.

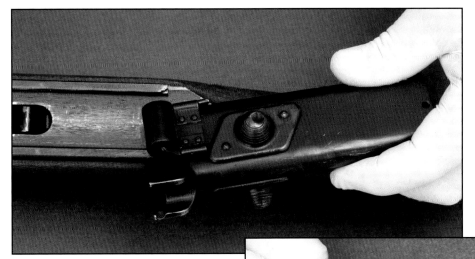

STEP 5

The entire unit of cover, bolt carrier and bolt is now slid back and off the receiver rails to the rear.

STEP 6

With this unit upside down on the bench, the bolt is rolled up as shown in the photo at the right and lifted out of the bolt carrier.

STEP 7

The bolt carrier and dust cover are now held tightly against a block of wood (as shown in the photo) and the button (see arrow) is pressed. This releases the recoil spring, so care is needed as it is under considerable tension.

STEP 8

The bolt carrier slides out of the dust cover. The rod in the center of the photograph is the recoil spring guide.

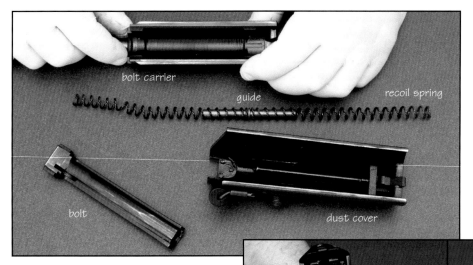

bolt carrier
guide
recoil spring
bolt
dust cover

STEP 9

The disassembled dust cover, bolt carrier, bolt and recoil spring with its guide.

REASSEMBLY HIGHLIGHTS:

A rod of some sort, in this case a screwdriver extension, is used to press the bolt carrier far enough into the dust cover for the button on the end to engage. It takes both hands to compress the recoil spring.

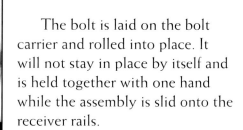

The bolt is laid on the bolt carrier and rolled into place. It will not stay in place by itself and is held together with one hand while the assembly is slid onto the receiver rails.

The bolt will catch on the hammer, which has to be slightly depressed with a finger in order for the assembly to slide forward. The block at the end of the receiver is returned, the dust cover pushed against it and the safety moved to the "off" position (see inset). *The bolt carrier and bolt will then slam forward so it is important to keep fingers clear.*

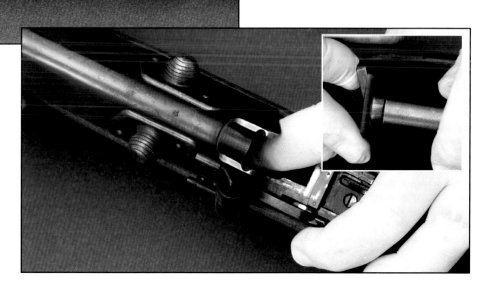

STEP 1

The rifle we have selected to disassemble is a Venezuelan contract SAFN 49 made by Fabrique Nationale. In this case, we have chosen to cover only the field stripping of this arm as further disassembly rapidly enters the realm of gunsmithing.

With the rifle pointed in a safe direction, the first step is to cock the rifle by pulling back on the bolt carrier handle, while making sure that the magazine and chamber are empty.

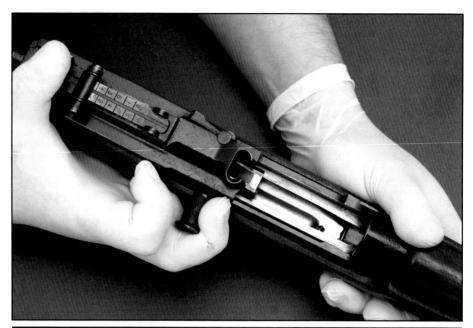

STEP 2

The bolt carrier is then allowed to slide forward until it is in the closed position.

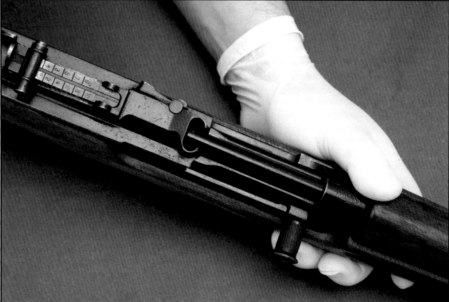

STEP 3

The locking key behind the rear sight on the bolt carrier is rotated 90 degrees into the upright position shown at the right.

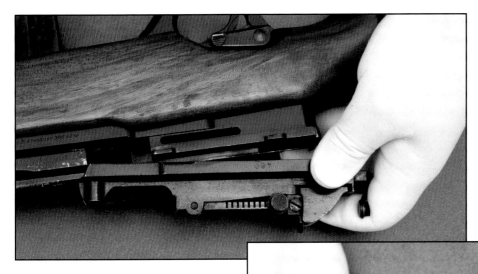

STEP 4

With the locking key upright, the bolt carrier is pushed forward to slightly compress the recoil springs and lifted up at the rear.

STEP 5

In order to be lifted off the rifle, the bolt carrier is slid back on the receiver rails until the bolt aligns with the clearance cuts in the receiver (see arrow).

STEP 6

The bolt carrier and the bolt are now lifted out of the rifle.

STEP 7

The bolt is removed from its carrier by sliding it back so that its lugs disengage.

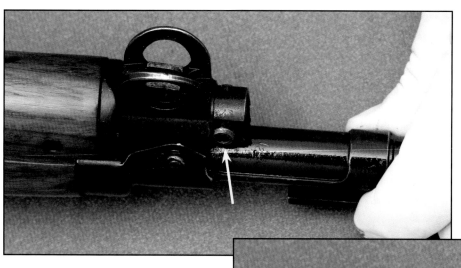

STEP 8

The gas piston is now removed by pressing in its catch (see arrow) and rotating it 1/4 turn towards the direction of the front sight. It may require a small punch to push in the catch if it is tight.

STEP 9

The gas cylinder plug is now removed.

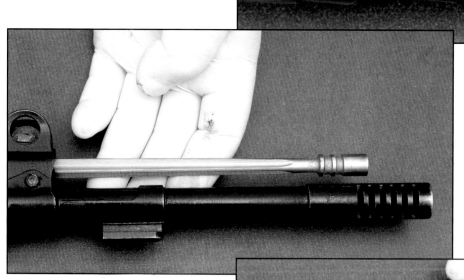

STEP 10

The gas piston is removed. It may be necessary to tilt the rifle down and shake it in order to slide it out.

STEP 11

If it failed to come out with the gas piston, the piston spring is now removed.

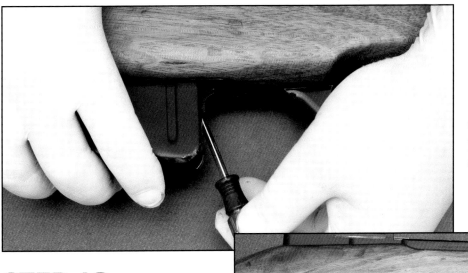

STEP 12

The magazine is removed by using a small screwdriver to gently pry open the catch located on the side facing the triggerguard.

STEP 13

The magazine and its spring are now released from the rifle. The FN 49 was designed to be loaded from stripper clips, so the magazine was not intended to be removed for reloading.

This completes the field stripping procedure.

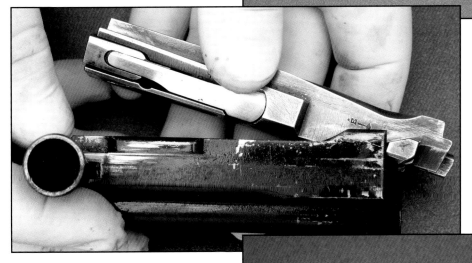

REASSEMBLY NOTES:

Reassembly is mostly a reversal of the field stripping steps. The photo at the left shows the bolt being returned to the bolt carrier. Once in place on the carrier, it is dropped into the receiver aligned

to the clearance cuts as shown in the photo. The bolt head sticks out about a half inch, just as can be seen in the picture at the right. The rear of the bolt carrier is then pushed down (compressing the spring) and the bolt and carrier easily slide forward. This makes room to return the receiver cover and recoil springs to their place.

The FN 49 Bolt

Disassembly:

The underside of the bolt as it came out of the rifle.

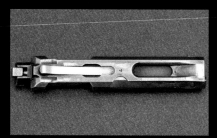

A view of the bolt fully disassembled.

The bolt stop is gently lifted with the blade of a screwdriver and pulled out of its slot.

Reassembly:

The mainspring is slipped onto the firing pin and both are slid into the bolt as shown.

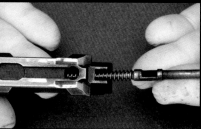

The extractor spring is gently lifted with the blade of a screwdriver and rotated (like the hands of a clock) ninety degrees up in the direction shown in the photo.

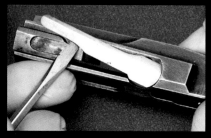

Pushing the firing pin in (see thumb), the extractor spring is returned to its place as shown.

With the extractor spring rotated up as described in the last step and shown in the inset here, the extractor is lifted out (see main view).

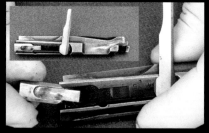

The extractor is then slid back into its groove and the extractor spring is rotated down to the horizontal position in order to hold it in place.

The rear of the firing pin is pushed down (see hand on the right) and the extractor spring is lifted out of the bolt (see hand on the left).

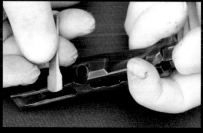

The firing pin stop is pushed into its groove. This can be a tight fit. The inset photo shows it in its final position.

The firing pin and spring are now taken out of the bolt. Note that this is a one-piece firing pin, which has often been replaced with an improved two-piece model.

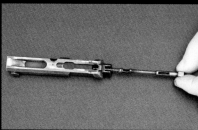

This is the bolt reassembled, in this case showing the extractor and extractor spring in their final positions.

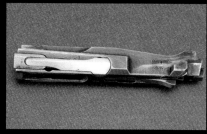

The AK47

STEP 1

Since most collectors are not legally able to acquire a true AK47 in its fully automatic state, we have chosen to disassemble one of the many semiautomatic versions that are currently available. The model we chose was an M70B1 by Century International Arms (www.centuryarms.com), which is a fixed-stock (rather than a folding-stock) variety. Making sure to keep the weapon pointed in a safe direction, and being careful not to touch the trigger, the magazine is removed.

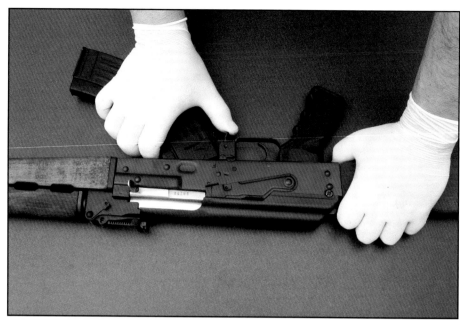

STEP 2

The bolt is pulled back to confirm that the chamber is empty and that the gun is not loaded.

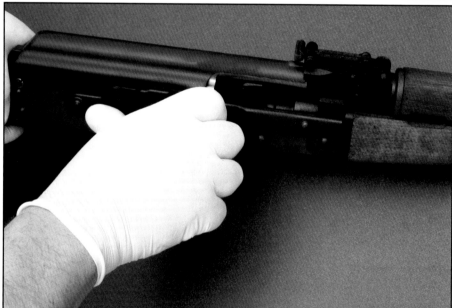

STEP 3

The cleaning rod is removed by lifting its end so that it clears the slot (see arrow) and pulling it forward. Note that removing the cleaning rod is not necessary to disassemble the rifle further and this step might easily have been left out.

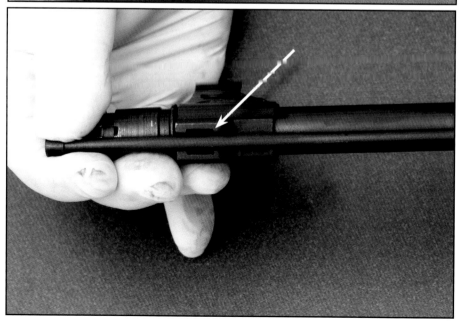

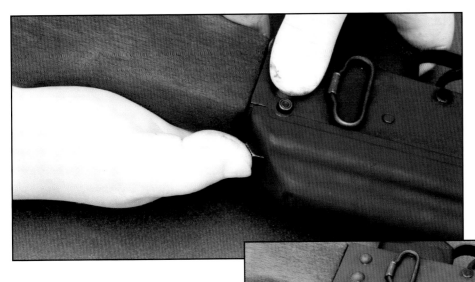

STEP 4

The button on the left side of the receiver is pressed. While holding it down, the rectangular button at the back of the receiver cover is also pressed. The first button is released, which should hold the second button in its depressed position.

STEP 5

The receiver cover is now lifted off, pulling it up and back from the rear.

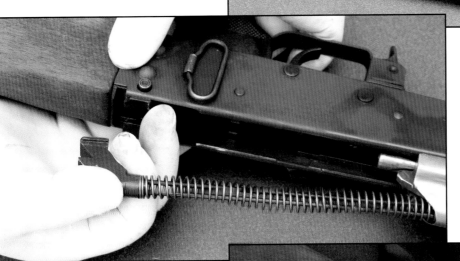

STEP 6

The recoil spring assembly is pushed forward by the rectangular button until it clears its slot and comes free. It is now pulled from the rifle.

STEP 7

The bolt assembly is pulled back and lifted out of the receiver.

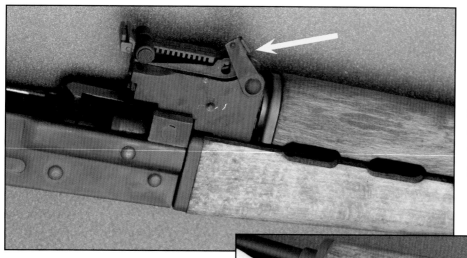

STEP 8

The lever on the side of the rear sight is rotated up to the 10 o'clock position as shown. Note that this will usually scratch the rifle's finish (also as shown).

STEP 9

The handguard and its integral gas tube are now lifted off the rifle, pulling up from the wide end near the sight.

STEP 10

This is the extent of a normal disassembly for one of these rifles. The remainder of the parts are mostly held together with rivets. Note, however, the interesting trigger spring assembly shown at the left.

REASSEMBLY

Reassembly is basically a reversal of the disassembly steps. The receiver cover went back on with the rectangular button on the end of the recoil assembly in its forward position. With the cover put in place, the circular button on the receiver was pressed so the rectangular button popped out of its hole.

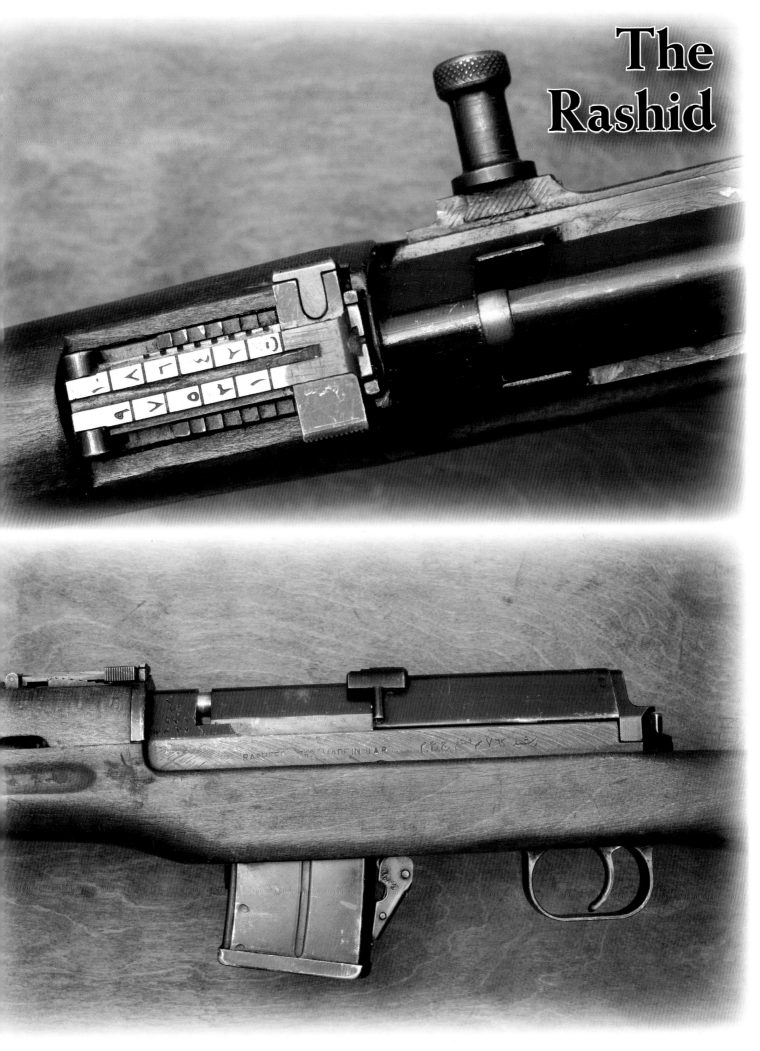

The
Rashid

STEP 1

The Rashid is an Egyptian-made hybrid utilizing elements of the SKS (see folding bayonet photo, top right) and the previous Egyptian military rifle, the Hakim.

The first step in stripping, as always, is to point it in a safe direction, open the action and confirm that the magazine and chamber are empty.

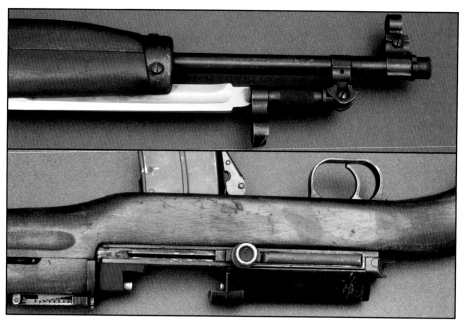

STEP 2

The magazine is released by rotating the latch shown here and pressing gently towards the magazine while pulling the magazine out of the rifle.

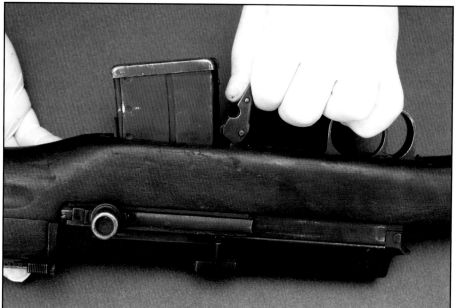

STEP 3

The dust cover is pulled forward and held with one hand while the safety is moved to the middle position and the block at the end of the receiver lifted out of its hole and set aside.

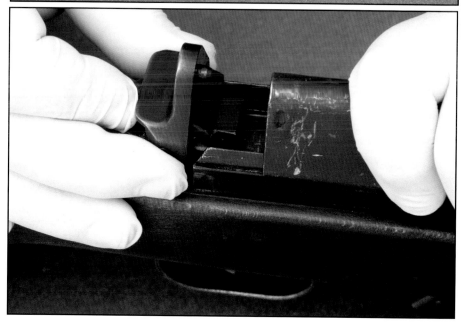

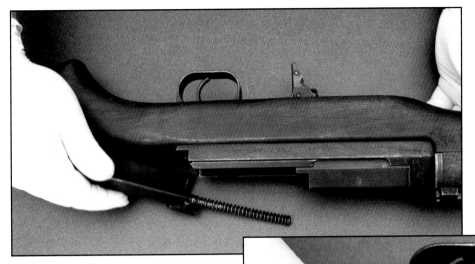

STEP 4

The dust cover is then slid back off the receiver, taking the recoil springs with it.

STEP 5

The bolt carrier and bolt are slid back and off the receiver.

STEP 6

The bolt is removed from the carrier by twisting it, as shown at the left, and lifting it out of the carrier.

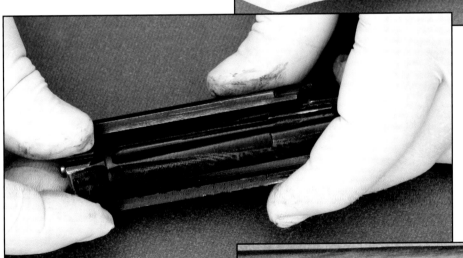

STEP 7

This completes field stripping the Rashid. The trigger group can be removed (only if necessary... it's hard to put back in) by loosening its three retaining screws. The screws, held in place with tiny springs, can only be moved about 1/4 turn at a time. The trigger group is not meant to be disassembled except by gunsmiths.

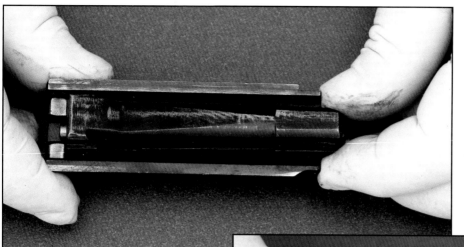

REASSEMBLY:

STEP 8
The bolt is placed back into the bolt carrier.

STEP 9
The bolt and carrier are slid onto the receiver rails. The hammer must be pushed down slightly (see finger in photo) for the bolt to pass over it.

STEP 10
The dust cover and recoil springs are now slid onto the receiver rail and pushed up against the bolt carrier.

STEP 11
While the bolt carrier is held in place, the block at the end of the receiver is returned to its hole and the rifle is now reassembled.

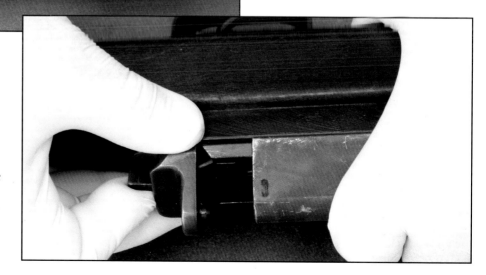